Bellini, Brunst, Jähnke (Eds.)

Current Issues in IT Security

Schriftenreihe des Max-Planck-Instituts für
ausländisches und internationales Strafrecht

Interdisziplinäre Forschungen
aus Strafrecht und Kriminologie

Herausgegeben von Hans-Jörg Albrecht
und Ulrich Sieber

Band I 17

Max-Planck-Institut für ausländisches
und internationales Strafrecht

Current Issues in IT Security

Proceedings of the interdisciplinary conference in
Freiburg i. Br./Germany, May 12-14, 2009

Bellini, Brunst, Jähnke (Eds.)

Duncker & Humblot · Berlin

Bibliografische Information der Deutschen Nationalbibliothek

Die Deutsche Nationalbibliothek verzeichnet diese Publikation in der Deutschen Nationalbibliografie; detaillierte bibliografische Daten sind im Internet über http://dnb.d-nb.de abrufbar.

c/o Max-Planck-Institut für ausländisches und internationales Strafrecht
Günterstalstraße 73, 79100 Freiburg i.Br.
http://www.mpicc.de
Vertrieb in Gemeinschaft mit Duncker & Humblot GmbH, Berlin
http://www.duncker-humblot.de

Titelbild: Dr. Phillip Brunst unter Verwendung einer Grafik von FlavioTakemoto
(flaivoloka/stock.xchng)
Druck: Stückle Druck und Verlag, Stückle-Straße 1, 77955 Ettenheim
Printed in Germany

ISSN 1862-7625
ISBN 978-3-86113-110-6 (Max-Planck-Institut)
ISBN 978-3-428-13516-5 (Duncker & Humblot)

Gedruckt auf alterungsbeständigem (säurefreiem) Papier
entsprechend ISO 9706

Preface

IT Security is an important issue, not only in practice but also in academia. The "Current Issues in IT Security" conference brought together researchers and practitioners from various disciplines, including IT professionals, lawyers, law enforcement and intelligence officers, judges, prosecutors, forensic specialists, and psychologists, and enabled them to share their expertise and insights on contemporary security issues.

The editors would like to express their gratitude to both directors of the Max Planck Institute for Foreign and International Criminal Law for their support of the conference. Prof. Dr. Dr. h.c. *Hans-Joerg Albrecht* and Prof. Dr. Dr. h.c. mult. *Ulrich Sieber* generously provided the funds needed to invite internationally renowned speakers to the conference and to publish this volume of conference proceedings in the interdisciplinary series of the Institute. The editors would also like to thank *Chris Murphy*, who not only proofread all the papers, but also provided valuable help and suggestions for the authors.

Overall, the conference highlighted the importance of an interdisciplinary approach to security-related issues. It is therefore our hope that many interesting projects will be developed together in the future to deepen the insights and findings into the numerous issues that are represented in this volume.

Freiburg, July 2010

Marcello Bellini *Phillip Brunst* *Jochen Jähnke*

Table of Contents

PHILLIP BRUNST

Contemporary Questions in IT Security

Information technology in general, the risks deriving from it as well as different legal issues in this context have been in the focus of the Max Planck Institute for Foreign and International Criminal Law for quite some time now. They form one of the research topics that closely bring together jurists, criminologists, IT specialists as well as many other disciplines. The Institute's Department of Criminology, led by Prof. Dr. Dr. h.c. *Hans-Jörg Albrecht*, for example, has worked extensively on dragnet investigations (Pehl, 2008), conducted several highly recognized studies on the disclosure of traffic and content data (Albrecht et al., 2003, Albrecht et al., 2008) and covert investigation measures on telecommunications in general. The Department of Criminal Law, led by Prof. Dr. Dr. h.c. *Ulrich Sieber*, features a dedicated section that continuously conducts research on different matters of information law. In the past, especially the topics of the extraterritorial prosecution of cybercrime (Sieber, 2006), blocking orders against so-called "illegal contents" (Sieber and Nolde, 2008), the phenomena of cybercrime and legal tools to combat them (Gercke and Brunst, 2009), anonymity on the Internet (Brunst, 2009) as well as terrorist use of the Internet (Brunst, 2008) have been in the focus of the section.

I. Concept of the Conference

In many of the Institute's projects the importance of IT security has become obvious since it is a core component in the fight against cybercrime and for the protection of confidentiality, availability, and integrity of computer systems and computer data. The idea to organize a workshop on this issue was therefore already born several years ago. In the beginning, however, these events were mainly aimed at IT personnel, especially from within the Max Planck Society. The interest of other groups, e.g. external professionals, law enforcement agencies, public prosecutors or forensic investigators, however steadily increased during the workshops that took place every two to three years. For the year 2009 it was therefore decided to organize the former workshop as a truly international and interdisciplinary conference. During the three-day-event from 12 to 14 May 2009, four different building blocks highlighted the different aspects of IT security and its importance for various disciplines. This volume of conference proceeding is an excerpt of the topics that were covered during the conference.

First Building Block: Technical Issues of IT Security

The first building block highlighted the technical issues of IT security. It showed that IT systems no longer only serve as a mere working environment. Instead, computers and IT infrastructure have become the very backbone of society. They connect and run, for example, power grids, airports and a large part of our economy. Vulnerable systems therefore pose a risk not only to individuals or companies, but to society in general. This was shown impressively by *Dirk von Suchodoletz*, who illustrated current issues of GSM and DECT security not only in theory, but also in practice. The same is true for *Jochen Jähnke*, who approached the topic from the viewpoint of his everyday work: What would an intruder do in order to (illegally) access the computer systems of an internationally renowned research facility? What would have to be done in order to prevent this? Apart from these two presentations that are included in this volume, *Andreas Mayer* explained the issues of next generation firewalls, *Martin Fillers* went into the weaknesses of notebook security (and showed possible solutions), and *Markus Wöhrle* talked on security issues concerning international speech and data communication.

Second Building Block: Victims of Cybercrime

The second building block looked at the victims of cybercrime. Interestingly enough, the impact of cybercrime remains one of the unsolved questions of IT security. Many individuals are not even aware that they are victims of computer crime at all. Businesses, on the other hand, often don't report detected cases, either because they fear setbacks vis-à-vis their competitors or because they do not know to whom to report. The highlighting of questions regarding the extent of victimization was therefore an important task of the conference. An internationally highly recognized expert in this field is *Ramona Rantala*, who explained her statistical findings in a study on cybercrime against businesses. *David Wall*, whose article can be found in this volume as well, talked on the organization of online crime and showed the background of a highly professionalized business. Finally, *Hans-Peter Merkel* gave a case-study on mass SMS chat fraud where victims have paid great amounts of money in the hope to find the love of their lives only to find out later that they have been scammed. The practical impact, especially before court, still remains to be seen.

Third Building Block: Outlook into the Future

The third building block dared to look into the future and tried to assess the risks that still lay ahead. *Jan Spoenle* picked up on the theme of *David Wall* from the previous block and gave an outlook on the cycle of organized cyber crime where different branches of criminal behavior closely work together, thereby creating a completely new level of danger. *Marco Gercke* evaluated attacks on critical infrastructure and gave an insight not only into possible future terrorist attacks, but also of everyday perpetrators who just might be interested in openly accessible information. *Gerhard Schneider* brought up the topic of cloud computing and showed that this new technology is not only fascinating and provides great possibilities, but that data protection and dangers of an international spreading of resources still need to be researched in more depth. *Lauren Saadat* gave an insight into the issue of privacy and cyber security, especially from the viewpoint of a U.S. government agency.

Fourth Building Block: Control

The fourth building block took into account the question of control and the implications of IT security in businesses and state policy. *Amir Alsbih*, for example, illustrated the problems of an abuse department of a privately owned company and *Meinrad Rombach* brought up the question to what extent laypersons should (or can) be made responsible for IT security. *Katalin Parti* looked at the change in danger-awareness while *Ales Zavrsnik* analyzed the question of whether criminal justice systems currently tend to overreact in the sight of cyber security threats. Lastly, *Soumyo Moitra* looked at questions of Internet policy and security management from a statistical standpoint.

We have asked not only speakers, but also participants if they would like to contribute to this volume of conference proceedings. We are therefore very happy to include an interesting article by *Dominik Brodowski* on the EU perspective on cybercrime and cybercrime investigations as well.

II. Feedback to the Conference

In order to get unbiased feedback as well as impulses for future conferences in this area, the organizers have set up an anonymous web-based feedback form and asked all participants to fill it out. Although not everybody followed this request, the results look very promising.

The idea not to focus on only a limited set of topics but a broad range of issues was regarded either as very good or good by 92% of all attendees who filled out the questionnaire (approx. 1/3 of all attendees). The rate regarding the question whether the expectations of the participants could actually be met was even higher. The feedback regarding conference rooms, accommodation, food and beverages as well as the overall atmosphere during the conference was also extremely positive. Overall, 92% would recommend the conference to their colleagues.

A question that arises before every conference regards the ratio between presentation time, discussion time, and breaks. Should presenters be given a greater amount of time in order to go into more details, with the obvious drawback of being able to include only a smaller number of speakers, or should lectures be seen more as short impulses for a longer discussion? How much time should be allocated for breaks, i.e. opportunities to get in touch with each other and to create new contact networks? For this conference the organizers decided to prefer short presentations (approx. 20-30 minutes) followed by a discussion of approx. 20 minutes and a 10-minute break in order to prepare for the next lecture. 83% of the participants found the length of the presentations perfect and 66% were satisfied with the time for the breaks. However, 42% wished to have more time for discussion.

The survey also asked participants what subjects should be included in future conferences. The question of filtering and its side effects was brought up in this context. Furthermore, participants wished to go more into the area of experience in investigation of cybercrime and data protection law. Referring to the latter, it was also asked if a more regional approach, i.e. comparison of data protection in different countries was possible. Finally, the wish was expressed to discuss some of the consequences for the topics presented to the Max Planck Society.

III. Following Activities

The "information law" section together with other interested internal Institute collaborators (namely *Jochen Jähnke* and *Marcello Bellini*) and external researchers of different disciplines (especially *David Wall* and *Soumyo Moitra*) began to discuss and conduct further research on some of the topics that were debated upon during the conference. The results of these activities, as well as additional aspects of the research by authors of this volume, will be published in the near future.

The conference as such has – this time, as previously – proven a great chance for researchers and practitioners of various disciplines to come together and discuss relevant issues from various angles. The next international conference on IT security is currently planned in the year 2011. The organizers hope that as many participants from the last event as possible can engage again in this conference so that not only the current focus is analyzed, but a more long-term perspective on the IT security situation can be brought into view.

The Call for Papers as well as all other information regarding the conference will be published on the MPI Web site at http://www.mpicc.de.

References

- ALBRECHT, H.-J., DORSCH, C. & KRÜPE, C. 2003. Rechtswirklichkeit und Effizienz der Überwachung der Telekommunikation nach den §§ 100a, 100b, StPO und anderer verdeckter Ermittlungsmaßnahmen. Eine rechtstatsächliche Untersuchung im Auftrag des Bundesministeriums der Justiz, Freiburg im Breisgau, Ed. Iuscrim Max-Planck-Inst. für Ausländisches und Internat. Strafrecht.
- ALBRECHT, H.-J., GRAFE, A. & KILCHLING, M. 2008. Rechtswirklichkeit der Auskunftserteilung über Telekommunikationsverbindungsdaten nach §§ 100g, 100h StPO. Forschungsbericht im Auftrag des Bundesministeriums der Justiz, Freiburg i. Br., Max-Planck-Institut für Ausländisches und Internationales Strafrecht.
- BRUNST, P. W. 2008. Use of the Internet by Terrorists – A Threat Analysis. In: CENTRE OF EXCELLENCE – DEFENCE AGAINST TERRORISM (ed.) Responses to Cyber Terrorism. Amsterdam: IOS Press.
- BRUNST, P. W. 2009. Anonymität im Internet - rechtliche und tatsächliche Rahmenbedingungen. Zum Spannungsfeld zwischen einem Recht auf Anonymität bei der elektronischen Kommunikation und den Möglichkeiten zur Identifizierung und Strafverfolgung, Berlin, Duncker & Humblot.
- GERCKE, M. & BRUNST, P. W. 2009. Praxishandbuch Internetstrafrecht, Kohlhammer.
- PEHL, D. 2008. Die Implementation der Rasterfahndung. Eine empirische Untersuchung zur Anwendung, Umsetzung und Wirkung der gesetzlichen Regelungen zur operativen Informationserhebung durch Rasterfahndung. Diss., Duncker & Humblot.
- SIEBER, U. 2006. Cybercrime and Jurisdiction in Germany. The Present Situation and the Need for New Solutions. In: KOOPS, B.-J. & BRENNER, S. (eds.) Cybercrime and Jurisdiction. Leiden.
- SIEBER, U. & NOLDE, M. 2008. Sperrverfügungen im Internet. Nationale Rechtsdurchsetzung im globalen Cyberspace?, Berlin, Duncker & Humblot.

Dirk von Suchodoletz

GSM and DECT Security

Recent Hardware and Software Developments Uncover Mobile Telephony Security Flaws and Privacy Issues

Wireless communication technologies like the world wide deployed GSM mobile phone networks or the popular home telephony standard DECT are threatened by several types of possible attacks because of poorly implemented security features. These technologies offer new freedom and flexibility, triggering new services and applications but may have downsides like being massively surveillable intruding into one's own private sphere. After x-raying the Internet security-wise, security experts get more and more interested in popular services. New types of generic radio channel development hardware and more powerful computers offer a wide range of new insights. A range of experiments run at the professorship demonstrate the simplicity of running a proper looking GSM cell, intercept communication and passively recording conversations for later decryption. These setups are typically operated by security experts but could be easily duplicated by attackers with standard computer knowledge. Thus many make-believe protection schemes may turn out to be problematic. Consequently, many new applications like sending and receiving banking PINs via phone should be rethought.

I. Changing Worlds

The telecommunications scene has significantly changed in the last 20 years. Hardly anyone still remembers the limited selection of chunky wired telephones which had to be leased from the Federal Mail & Telecommunication at the time. The world was structured simply: connections were allocated depending strongly on geographic location to their respective users like companies, organizations, authorities or individuals. Telephone calls could be placed either at home or from work, in rarer cases also anonymously from one of the public telephones. These were installed in larger quantities in cities as well as in villages with a population of just a few hundred people. Only a limited political and business elite had the possibility to make mobile telephone calls. This made the world easy from the view point of the users of this technology as well as from the regulatory side. The operator of this network was the state; the privacy of the network users was protected through the law on the privacy of telecommunications (TKG, 2009).

This traditional world was detached in the last two decades through a number of technological developments and significant changes of the framework: in most European countries, the liberalization and privatization of the telephone networks took their exit with the development of the mobile phone network. Instead of one central state-run provider typically a number of independent providers started using the mutually defined European mobile phone standard GSM (GSMA, 2009). A substantial part of this article will thus deal with the security implications of these networks of the so-called second generation.

In the next step of the liberalization the (part-)privatization of the former state telephone companies followed. Just like there were more mobile telephony providers, it was intended to have more players in the market for landline telephone connections. This meant that suddenly not all national calls were routed within the network of a single telephone company but instead could involve a number of different companies to connect the call.

An initial impact was the new freedom of the hard-wired traditional telephones. Cordless handsets quickly gained popularity. Here with the DECT standard – taken into consideration too – another digital communication standard spread comprehensively. The change is still being accelerated through the ongoing development which is pushed by the Internet. A strong convergence of both data and telephony networks is under way, which until the start of the millennium were largely separated. Whilst the Internet or Voice-over-IP do not stand in the centre point of consideration, they should however be mentioned here too.

The price fall resulting from the liberalization and the new possibilities of the constant ability to communicate have brought the mobile networks significant growth and in most countries the number of mobile phone users is substantially higher than the number of landline owners. Simple handsets are now available for rather small amounts of money, so that in particular the number of mobile phone users increased exponentially in developing countries.

A. The New Mobile Freedom ...

Mobile networks for telecommunication offer new freedom. A user in the network, when they have their phone switched on, can make and receive calls under a uniform number regardless of location. For this the mobile telephone registers itself on "entering" the network and updates regularly with change of location over a certain radius (Bettstätter et al., 2009: 152ff). For every entity a worldwide unique ID is used which is stored on the SIM-card, a small piece of discrete crypto-hardware. On this ID – for the users the central aspect – the telephone number is linked on which they can be contacted. This concept of the separation into mobile hardware and the authentication and crypto device was a significant innovation of the new digital mobile networks (Bettstätter et al., 2009: 43ff).

Through worldwide roaming agreements – the interoperability beginning with European but later also worldwide mobile networks – the reachability by phone is sustained even when moving outside national borders. This has significant implications for network operators, users and third parties (for example, law enforcement authorities). The communication network of the respectively involved providers must know where the individual users is located to fulfil requirements such as routing and delivering an incoming call or SMS. As a result, information about the user also accrues beyond their network provider.

B. ... and Her Little Sister

Visiting electronic communications shops online or offline indicates the high popularity of cordless landline end devices. Even if the now over one hundred year old specified analogue connection is now on its last mile to be replaced by TV-cable or VOIP, the corresponding Internet Access Device offers the same compatible connecting socket like the old copper wires did a century before. Therefore a dominating market for this type of device continues to exist, that uses the DECT standard (Olanders, 1994). This allows the owner to conduct landline calls in a perimeter of a few hundreds meters around their base station. While the range of the classic telephone was limited by the length of the cable, the "visibility" and with it also the potential access to a telephone connection goes much further than the borders of one's own home, the premises of organizations, companies or authorities.

II. Technical Background

Both GSM and DECT replaced their predecessor technologies with the declared goal, to ensure the safety from interception of cordless communication. For a long time hardly anyone contradicted the pretences from the involved industry consortia.

For a better understanding of the potential threat and possible attack scenarios this chapter gives a short overview to the technical background of the network standards GSM and DECT. While with DECT the interception or potential misuse of a connection stand in the front line, the almost complete covering infrastructure of GSM (GSMA, 2009) offers a wider range of additional threats. The significantly changed habits of today's people to carry a phone nearly everywhere offers new types of location based services and risks. Thus two different kinds of attacks can be distinguished, the types aiming directly on the calls and the ones trying to uncover location or other whereabouts of communication.

A. Groupe Special Mobile (GSM)

GSM (originally Groupe Special Mobile, after worldwide adaptation now: Global System for Mobile Communications) describes a wireless telephony standard for both digital signalling and speech or data transport. As there were different, incompatible predecessors like the C Netz in Germany, NMT or TACS in other countries it is considered a second generation (2G) mobile phone system (Bettstätter et al., 2009: 5). With more then 3 billion people using GSM phones in more then 219 countries (GSMA, 2009) it serves worldwide over three thirds of the mobile telecommunication market. Interestingly, the standard defines one worldwide emergency telephone number, 911 in the US (E911) and 112 in Europe (E112), which makes sense in the moment every device placing an emergency call could be located (Zhao, 2002).

1. GSM Infrastructure

The GSM infrastructure is logically split into three subsystems (Fig. 1): The radio subsystem covers the main speciality of mobile telephony network the air interface and involved components. On the user side the Mobile Station (MS) consists of two parts: The Mobile Equipment (ME) or terminal and the Subscribers Identity Module (SIM). The SIM is a detachable smart card storing user's subscription information, phone book and other data like the IMSI cryptographically locked and secured by a PIN. Additionally it contains cryptographic routines like A3 and A5 for authentication and speech encryption (Nohl, Krissler, 2009). This design allows the user to replace the hardware without negotiating to the provider as it is identified solely by the SIM. The network operator's side consists of the Base Transceiver Stations (BTS) and the Base Station Controllers (BSC) managing several BTS.

The network and switching subsystem (or simply the core network) is comparable to the standard digital landline telephony systems like ISDN supporting the interoperability with other so called Intelligent Networks (IN). The INs deploy the vendor independent Signalling System 7 (SS7) protocols and standards for call setup and routing (Engel, 2008). The subsystem contains the Home Location Register which stores the subscriber's individual contract parameters and maps e.g. the International Mobile Subscriber Identity (IMSI) to a national telephone number.

The operation and maintenance subsystem handles the subscriber authentication, the whole system management and monitoring. The authentication centre subsystem may operate an Equipment ID Register (EIR) which contains all International Mobile Equipment Identity of the Devices handed out by the provider. It was introduced for example, to track down stolen equipment and lock it off from the network.

Most GSM networks operate in the 900MHz or 1800MHz bands. Some countries like Canada and the United States use the 850MHz and 1900MHz bands as the standard bands were already assigned to other services. A typical nowadays mobile telephone is able to operate in all four frequencies. GSM is a cell-based network using different sub bands in adjacent cells. The cell diameter in the 850, 900MHz bands could reach up to 35km, in the higher frequency bands around 8km.

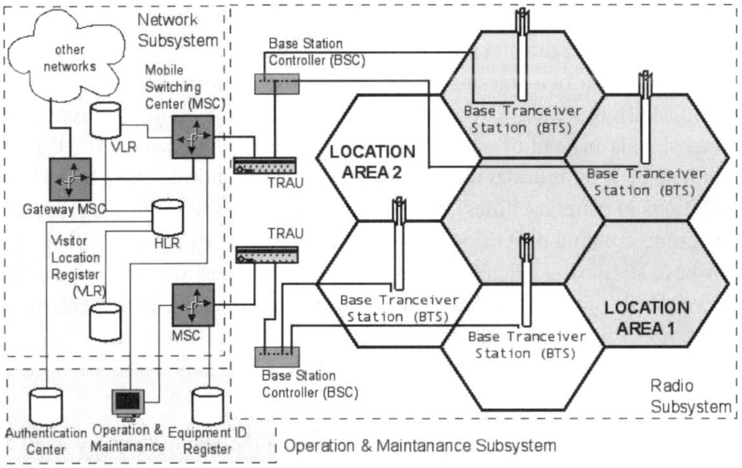

Figure: The GSM network is split into three logical subsystems. Not all components have to be implemented to run a working infrastructure.

B. Locating Mobile Phones

While in landline telephony it is pretty easy to locate the origin of an emergency call, it is quite different in the mobile world. The United States Federal Communications Commission (FCC) and later on the European Commission have required that mobile communication providers should be able to accurately locate mobile emergency calls via E112 (Bitzi, Ingensand, 2001). As a consequence, practical mobile phone positioning technologies were researched from the late 1990s onwards (Drane et al., 1998). Obtaining one's location when moving around got quite popular with the GPS navigation devices. As GPS has some shortcomings, especially indoors or in densely populated areas, positioning based on existing mobile communications infrastructure gained quite interest amongst academics. As GPS has no back channel for online interaction and update of location relevant information the telecommunication providers hopped on the hype and hoping to find with so-called Location Based Services (Magon, 2009) the next mega-seller to utilize their data networks (Rao, Minakakis, 2004).

There are a variety of ways to derive mobile equipment location from the view point of the infrastructure operation. The most important ones are Cell ID, Time of Arrival, Time Difference of Arrival and Angle of Arrival.

The simplest way to locate a mobile phone is to find its cell area as it typically connects to the nearest BTS. The location of the antenna approximates the mobile device. As electromagnetic signal travels at specific speed the distance between the mobile device and the base station could be calculated from it. A mobile phone is attached to one station but the others in the vicinity observe it too. Thus it would be possible with more than two stations to triangulate the location of the mobile device. The Time Difference of Arrival approach makes use of time difference between arrived signals instead of absolute time (Gustafsson, Gunnarsson, 2003). A signal is emitted by a mobile device at an unknown time and received by at least three base stations at different times. Applying trilateration, the location of the mobile device can be computed: At first the time difference of signal arrival between each pair of base stations is calculated. Each difference places the device on a hyperbolic curve. With two of these curves the location of the mobile device can be computed unambiguously, as it is the intersection of the two hyperbolic curves. Because many BTS use sectored antennas the angle of signals could be used in calculation (Gustafsson, Gunnarsson, 2005).

The radio subsystem measures distances of phones to the serving cell by itself to compensate for the propagation delay of the signal between the MS and BTS. The Timing Advance (TA) parameter is an 8bit value used to split the 35km radius into 64 virtual rings of roughly 550m in diameter (Bajada, 2003). The TA is regularly updated in active connections and sent from the infrastructure to each mobile phone.

Cell Origin and Timing Advance are methods in place already as needed for the operation of the radio network. The other techniques depend on very precise and well synchronized clocks in the radio subsystem infrastructure (Drane et al., 1998), which are typically not available yet.

The gained accuracy depends on the method used. A combination of different methods may improve localization. The typical resolution ranges from under 100 to 500m (Bitzi, Ingensand, 2001).

C. Digital Enhanced Cordless Telecommunications

DECT was originally developed by ETSI at the beginning of the 1990s. It is a wireless standard for digital portable phones, commonly used for domestic or corporate purposes (Olanders, 1994). The standard uses the 1880-1900MHz frequency band divided into 10 sub channels in Europe with 1,728kHz spacing and slightly different frequencies and channelling in other parts of the world. It is quite popular with an estimated 30 Million phones in Germany alone (Koberstein et al., 2009). The channels are dynamically allocated. The radius of a base station typically amounts to 30-50m operation depending on the environment, but 300m is possible with the standard equipment. The average transmission power rates at 10mW with 250mW peak in Europe and 4mW (100mW peak) in the US.

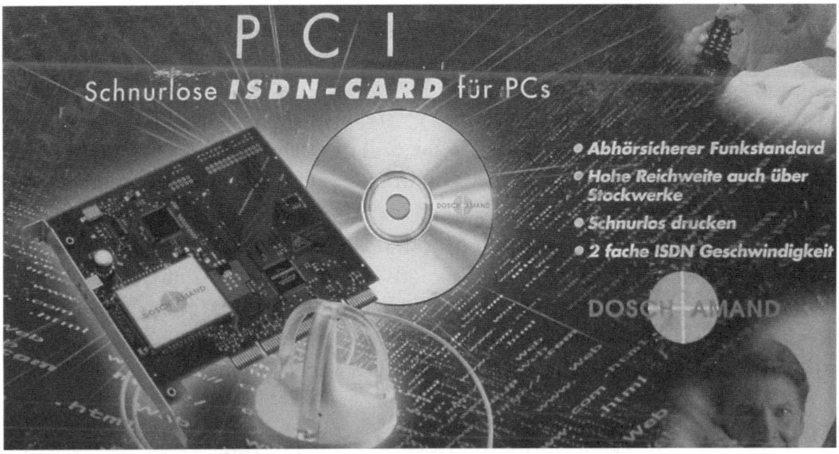

Figure: The industry is claiming DECT to be a tap-proof standard. The device shown could be deployed in a Linux system for analyzing and eavesdropping DECT systems.

The DECT standard could be extended in a way to provide the ability to access the mobile capability of telecommunication networks. It could be deployed to setup a multi cellular infrastructure allowing roaming across a wider area and the receiving and placement of calls within the covered area. This function could be found in some PBXs of larger businesses (Liveris et al., 1998).

III. Security Implications

Wireless networks face completely different requirements than cabled installations. Within the latter the physical access can easily be regulated and monitored. Electromagnetic waves can – even when they can't necessarily be deciphered – still be detected from large distances by special directed antennas and amplifying technology.

The comfortable times of the make-believe security are over: while for a long time the technical equipment was too expensive and interest wasn't awoken, the winds have since changed. Steady increases in computing power of even compacter devices and a number of special hardware components have caused the various networks to appear on the radar of security experts.

A. GSM Security and Privacy

As a ubiquitous infrastructure, GSM allows a wide range of measures to gain knowledge on persons and their communications without any tampering of the network (and even more with tampering). With the standard data collected by the mobile telecommunication providers for actual positioning and the storage of it requested by law for six months, two types of subscriber surveillance would be feasible. In real time surveillance every "step" of the mobile phone user is recorded. It would be possible to deploy the Cell of Origin and TA techniques to follow the monitored person in an accuracy of up to 50m. With the data recorded and stored during normal network operation it would be possible to recover the position of a mobile subscriber for a certain period of time. A rather well known case took place on the 23rd March, 2008, on a motorway near Oldenburg in Germany. A female was struck dead by a wooden log thrown from a bridge. Following the investigation, inspectors applied for and received access to call and SMS data of around 10,000 people making them possible suspects (Krempl, 2008).

1. Externally Triggered User Location

Interestingly no direct access to the mobile provider's databases is needed to estimate the position of a mobile subscriber. A simple SMS service is enough to determine the location using the underlying SS7 system. The Mobile Application Part (MAP) of the protocol defines functions for accessing the databases of the MSCs like the HLR and VLR. With these functions it is possible to place a subscriber within a location area typically covering parts of a city or several square kilometres in the country side. Of course this service is not open to everyone but could be used via special service providers for a few cents (Engel, 2008). Other companies like www.trackyourkid.de claim to track the location of children via Internet or as a mobile service. Many mobile phone providers offer similar services like O_2's "Handy-Finder". These providers typically do not disclose their technological back-end and do not necessarily inform a user that his phone just got tracked.

There are ongoing research projects using GSM communication to analyse traffic patterns. One of the typical tasks in traffic routing is the forecast of traffic jams. The University of Stuttgart together with Deutsche Telekom were involved in a research project analyzing the patterns of mobile phones travelling in cars on different routes to predict traffic jams. Similar projects were conducted in the Netherlands using the data from several providers (Asendorpf, 2008).

2. GSM Dissected

GSM is an open standard and the standardization documents are available for everyone to see. Through increasing computing power one does no longer even require specialised electronic circuits, but can operate on generic hardware, for example in development offering prototyping and debugging (Saha, 2008). Such a device is offered for sale, for example the company Ettus Research produces Universal Software Radio Peripherals (USRP). These are fast AD converters with multiple transmit and receive channel support (Ettus, 2010). The USRPs are coupled to a computer via USB or Ethernet for the sending and receiving of the digitalised signals for further processing. At this point the GNU Radio (GNURadio, 2010) open source libraries come into play for all common software radio needs, like signal processing constructs (optimized filters, FFTs, equalizers, timing recovery), various modulations (GMSK, PSK, QAM, OFDM, etc.), scheduling and error-correcting codes (Reed-Solomon, Viterbi, Turbo Codes).

Figure: The USRP of Ettus Research is just a fast analogue digital converter deployable for research and development of radio modulation and multiplexing. Displayed with a better timing source for improved operation in the GSM band.

The applications deploying these libraries could be developed in C++ or Python programming languages (GNU Radio, 2009). Depending on the complexity of such a setup of software and hardware, the possibility is offered to replicate the air interface of GSM and other standards (Welte, 2009). With a combined send and receive channel a BTS can be replicated. The configuration as a pure receiving station allows the setup of a passive network monitor (Airprobe, 2009). For a spectrum analysis of mobile bands, to determine on which frequencies base stations send, USRP/2 is offered. The signal is received and demodulated. The packets created can then we viewed by using special Wireshark plug-ins. With A5 encrypted voice packets a number of methods could be used to decrypt the data stream (Nohl, Krissler, 2009).

3. A GSM Micro Net

A small mobile cell can be setup as a pure software solution with the USRP, GNU Radio for the air interface and Asterisk PBX for the voice relay and authentication (Asterisk, 2010). Asterisk is a proven open source VoIP solution with different media gateway functionality built in. It identifies the mobile telephones registered in the cell given the IMSI on the installed SIM and links this when required to an internal SIP account.

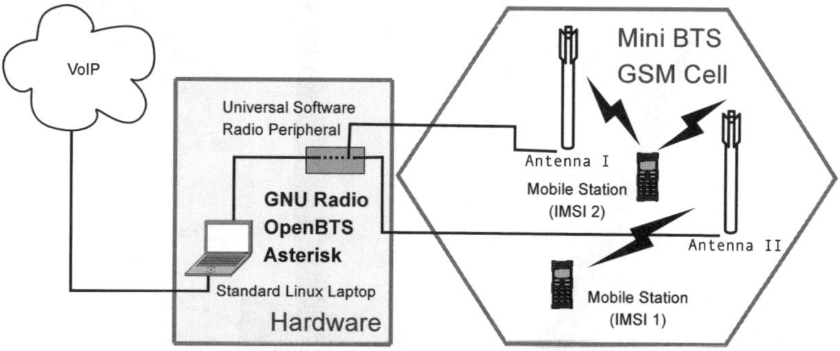

Figure: Not many components are needed to setup a mini GSM cell. The USRP is sending and receiving GSM signals in the 900MHz band; the rest is done by a standard off-the-shelf laptop running open source tools on Linux.

The mobile cell can be connected with the outside world with all Asterisk supported telephone protocols. In a cell which has up to eight active users, with considerably more passively registered mobile devices, solely the USRP and an average laptop are required. The latter takes over the signal encoding and decoding via GNU Radio and the operation of the Asterisk telephone system. Such a cell was created and successfully run with several GSM features like SMS and voice communication during several master theses running at the professorship and demonstrated at the security workshop in Freiburg 2009.

4. IMSI Catcher for the Masses

While the back-end infrastructure, which like a classic telephone network also decodes the calls, partially also transmits over a simple radio link, is akin to current WLAN setups, the path from the mobile end device and the access point (BTS) is encrypted. However the trust relationship is only one sided: the participant must trust the mobile network, only the network itself requires authentication of the participants. Using the previously introduced hardware and software components the step to implement an IMSI catcher (Meyer, Wetzel, 2004) is not far off. Brining this together, mobile networks can be simulated and one can listen to calls routed over them. The attacked victim would not notice this very quickly since only few mobile telephones show whether or not the air interface is even encrypted. While only the Federal Office of Criminal Investigation in Germany is allowed to use an IMSI catcher, it is a trivial device that could be created from standard hardware and open source software. A master thesis accomplished at the professorship demonstrated the feasibility and the ease of use of such a setup.

5. Compromising the Crypto Algorithms

Since the interception of cordless communication causes few problems, in the next step decrypting the data comes into the foreground. The vast majority of signalling occurs unencrypted, solely the voice connection and data services are secured on the path between MS and BTS (Moldal, Jorgensen, 2003), but not necessarily within the back-end infrastructure. For this the A5 algorithm is put into play from which weak points were demonstrated (Ekdahl, Johansson, 2001). The security of cryptographic algorithms is determined by the required time to reconstruct messages. Next to the optimization through mathematical findings and the application of rainbow tables (Nohl, Krissler, 2009), it can be shown, that the time can be reduced to a few hours or minutes using special hardware (Güneysu et al., 2008).

6. Using DECT like Sending Picture Postcards

The average end user is typically unaware of the security implications using DECT equipment. Like the minority of mobile telephones, DECT devices display whether the air interface is encrypted or not (Koberstein et al., 2009). Beside private communications, security relevant transactions could be overheard: Telling access PINs or credit card numbers and security codes to service people, navigating banking systems via DTMF, private information exchanged between physicians and pharmacist or their patients. With special equipment like directed antennas it would be possible to easily overhear DECT communications several hundred meters away without exposing the attacker. While costly equipment was originally required for DECT attacks, this equipment, and a Linux system, is now readily available (Heise, Serious Security Vulnerabilities, 2008). Several open source projects like dedected.org (Dedected, 2009; Welte, 2010), the planned adaptation of the Kismet tool to support DECT (Kismet, 2010) or research at universities demonstrate the weaknesses of today's systems (Mengele, 2009).

IV. Juridical Implications

Generally different classes of attacks with different implications could be identified. While the average user is interested in privacy and anti-fraud a mobile network provider focuses on uninterrupted business and unauthorized access.

While with DECT the interception security is in the front line, the GSM users have more to be concerned with. The stored movement data could be seen as problematic, even if they never leave the provider. The potential handover to interested third parties such as authorities, security firms or advertisers is definitely an issue for parts of the user base. Additionally the general privacy of communication is expected. Nobody should easily overhear ongoing calls or record them.

The military has seen the demand for a proper end-to-end encryption to protect the secrecy of communications (Moldal, Jorgensen, 2003). Only some high rank officials like the Chancellor in Germany use similar devices. But it is not openly discussed to protect the average user as the same technology might effectively lock off law enforcement agencies. It would be naïve to believe that the non-availability of secure mobile telecommunications would lock off organized crime, too.

Figure: Nearly all mobile phones could be connected to the fake GSM cell in the IMSI catcher experiments. Only the rather old Siemens S55 displayed the non-encrypted call placed during the tests.

Nearly every person, not only high level officials or managers, could be the victim of electronic eavesdropping. Private eyes could extend their arsenal on unfaithful spouses and 'computer kids' could get new fields of activity. Beside the technical point of view, some open issues in the juridical sphere are of interest: Is there a liability of the mobile communication companies to provide a secure communication channel? Should a trusted public key certificate infrastructure provided? How should structures which support proper public testing and proving of upcoming technology be implemented?

Another problematic field is the active and rather unregulated ecosystem of location services to track mobile devices. Most of those services do not inform the subscribers which location methods are used and tell tracked mobile phone users that their device was located.

V. Conclusions

Even when legal requirements protect against unauthorized senders on the frequency bands of GSM and DECT, this can easily suppress the monitoring of calls. The privacy of the calls which was originally understood as well protected is threatened through technical weaknesses. With the worldwide distributed GSM a particularly problematic aspect is added: Every mobile user and that is in the Western industrial countries almost everyone from a particular age, can be fairly easily monitored. These services are advertised actively by providers or third parties for typically a relatively small sum of money. The mass monitoring and storing of movement data is not blocked by any technical challenges and is even legally demanded. The hardware together with the open source software packages presented could help to uncover location techniques used by the different providers. There is a trade off between a highly desired accuracy for emergency calls and the mobile subscriber's privacy.

Should the legislative body allow in the future a proper end-to-end encryption as demanded by Nohl and Krissler (2009) to protect the privacy of mobile communications? At least the German government reacted and ordered more than a thousand devices offering end-to-end encryption. Interestingly, the GSM standard declares that mobile phones should inform the user of unencrypted call setup but this a feature configurable via SIM option and is typically switched off by service providers.

While lawmakers have voiced pressure for the content branch to compulsorily encrypt, the case is different for DECT. What will happen when via DECT anonymous calls with criminal relevance are conducted or information like the saved telephone book or call history are read by lawyers or companies?

Generally it is valid to state that the secrecy and sealing of security relevant technology does not solve the problem. On the contrary, the Mifare case (Heise, Mangelhafte Verschlüsselung, 2008; Krissler et al., 2008) has shown that the traffic companies and access providers have relied on a technology which now faces large and potentially also relevant economic problems. Instead of more secure, the position becomes, more absurd when the manufacturer of defective security technology complains about the release of weaknesses (Heise, Mifare Hersteller NXP verklagt,

2008). The establishment of the AES crypto standard demonstrates a good path to follow for future implementations: open request for proposals, discussion and active involvement of the security and research community.

While the considerations of this paper were oriented to the wireless infrastructure, the mobile devices themselves were mostly ignored. New challenges for network operation might appear if the firmware of the GSM controller is modified e.g. for sending rogue packets to start denial-of-service attacks. Thus Apple had to inform the FCC after its 2G iPhone was jailbroken.

References

- AIRPROBE, 2010. Air-interface analysis tool for the GSM [online]. [Accessed 10 April 2010]. Available from World Wide Web: <http://airprobe.org>
- ASENDORPF, D., 2008. Die nützlichen Verräter. Die Zeit Nr. 46 [online]. [Accessed 19 April 2010]. Available from World Wide Web: <http://www.zeit.de/2008/46/Autohandys>
- ASTERISK, 2010. The open source PBX and telephony platform [online]. [Accessed 15 April 2010]. Available from World Wide Web: <http://www.asterisk.org>
- BAJADA, J. 2003. Mobile Positioning for Location Dependent Services in GSM Networks [online]. [Accessed 5 April 2010]. Proceedings of CSAW 2003. Available from World Wide Web: <http://www.cs.um.edu.mt/~csaw/CSAW03/Proceedings/MobilePositioning.pdf>
- BETTSTÄTTER, C., EBERSPÄCHER, J., HARTMANN, C. & VÖGEL, HJ., 2009. GSM – Architecture, Protocols and Services. Chichester, West Sussex: Wiley.
- BITZI, P. & INGENSAND, H. 2001. Technologien der GSM-Positionierungsverfahren. AVN – 08-09/2001.
- DRANE, C., MACNAUGHTAN, M., SCOTT, C., 1998. Positioning GSM Telephones. IEEE Communications Magazine. Volume 36, Issue 4, April 1998. pages: 46 - 54, 59.
- deDECTed.org Project, 2010. Open source implementation of the DECT standard [online]. [Accessed 21 April 2010]. Available from World Wide Web: <https://dedected.org>
- EKDAHL, P., JOHANSSON, T., 2003. Another attack on A5/1. IEEE Transactions on Information Theory. Volume 49, Issue 1, Jan 2003, pages 284 – 289.
- ENGEL, T., 2008. Locating Mobile Phones using Signaling System # 7[online]. [Accessed 2 April 2010]. Available from World Wide Web: <http://events.ccc.de/congress/2008/Fahrplan/attachments/1262_25c3-locating-mobile-phones.pdf>
- ETTUS, 2010. Ettus Reseach LLC – USRP product family [online]. [Accessed 15 April 2010]. Available from World Wide Web: <http://www.ettus.com>
- GNURadio, 2010. Software toolkit for signal processing and building blocks to implement software radios [online]. [Accessed 19 April 2010]. Available from World Wide Web: <http://gnuradio.org>

- GSM ASSOCIATION 2009. GSM Associations website, About us [online]. [Accessed 9 August 2009]. Available from World Wide Web: <http://www.gsmworld.com/about-us/index.htm>
- GÜNEYSU, T., KASPER, T., NOVOTNÝ, M., PAAR, C. RUPP, A., 2008. Cryptanalysis with COPACOBANA. IEEE Transactions on Computers. Volume 57, Issue 11, pages 1498 – 1513.
- GUSTAFSSON, F., GUNNARSSON, F. 2005. Mobile positioning using wireless networks: possibilities and fundamental limitations based on available wireless network measurements. Signal Processing Magazine, IEEE. Volume 22, Issue 4, page 41- 53.
- GUSTAFSSON, F., GUNNARSSON, F. 2003. Positioning using time-difference of arrival measurements. Proceedings of IEEE International Conference on Acoustics, Speech, and Signal Processing. Volume 6. pages VI – 553-556.
- HEISE, 2008. Serious security vulnerabilities in DECT wireless telephony [online]. [Accessed 14 December 2009]. Available from World Wide Web: <http://www.h-online.com/security/25C3-Serious-security-vulnerabilities-in-DECT-wireless-telephony--/news/112326>
- HEISE, 2008. Mangelhafte Verschlüsselung bei vielen RFID-Karten [online]. [Accessed 9 September 2009]. Available from World Wide Web: <http://www.heise.de/security/25C3-Mangelhafte-Verschluesselung-bei-vielen-RFID-Karten--/news/meldung/121028>
- HEISE, 2008. Mifare-Hersteller NXP verklagt Sicherheitsforscher [online]. [Accessed 9 September 2009]. Available from World Wide Web: <http://www.heise.de/security/Mifare-Hersteller-NXP-verklagt-Sicherheitsforscher--/news/meldung/110782>
- KISMET, 2010. Wireless Network Detector [online]. [Accessed 15 April 2009]. Available from World Wide Web: <http://www.kismetwireless.net>
- KREMPL, S., 2008. Bedenken gegen „Rasterfahndung“ im Holzklotz-Fall. [online]. [Accessed 15 April 2001]. Available from World Wide Web: <http://www.heise.de/ newsticker/Bedenken-gegen-Rasterfahndung-im-Holzklotz-Fall--/meldung/113253>
- KOBERSTEIN, H., KURZ, F., MEIER B., 2009. Abhören leicht gemacht – Millionen Telefone sind unsicher [online]. [Accessed 9 September 2009]. Available from World Wide Web: <http://frontal21.zdf.de/ZDFde/inhalt/3/0,1872,7505859,00.html>
- KRISSLER, J., NOHL, K., PLÖTZ, H., 2008. Chiptease – Verschlüsselung eines führenden Bezahlkartensystems geknackt. ct 08/2008, pages 80 – 85.
- LIVERIS, A.D., GEORGANTAS, N.V., THEOLOGOU, M.E., 1998. DECT mobility support in a hybrid DECT-broadband ISDN environment. Third IEEE Symposium on Computers and Communications, 1998. pages: 235 – 239.
- MAGON, A., 2009. LBS, the ingredients and the alternatives [online]. [Accessed 12 September 2009]. Available from World Wide Web: <http://www.gisdevelopment.net/ technology/lbs/techlbs006pf.htm>.
- MENGELE, A., 2009. Security of Digital Enhanced Cordless Telecommunication (DECT) devices for residential use [online]. [Accessed 15 September 2009]. Available from World Wide Web: <http://www.cdc.informatik.tu-darmstadt.de/reports/reports/Alexandra_Mengele.diplom.pdf>

- MEYER, U., WETZEL, S., 2004. A man-in-the-middle attack on UMTS. Workshop on Wireless Security – Proceedings of the 3rd ACM workshop on Wireless security Philadelphia October 2004. Pages: 90 – 97.
- MOLDAL, L., JORGENSEN, T., 2003. End to end encryption in GSM, DECT and satellite networks using NSK200. IEE Seminar on Secure GSM and Beyond: End to End Security for Mobile Communications. Digest 2003/10059, pages: 5/1 – 5/5.
- NOHL, K., KRISSLER, S., 2009. Subverting the security base of GSM. HAR 2009 [online]. [Accessed 21 September 2009]. Available from World Wide Web: <https://har2009.org/program/attachments/119_GSM.A51.Cracking.Nohl.pdf>
- OLANDERS, P. 1994. DECT standardisation: status and future activities. Personal, Indoor and Mobile Radio Communications - 5th IEEE International Symposium on Wireless Networks - Catching the Mobile Future. Volume 4, pages:1064 – 1069.
- RAO, B., MINAKAKIS, L., 2004. Assessing the Business Impact of Location Based Services. Proceedings of the 37th Annual Hawaii International Conference on System Sciences. hicss, vol. 3, pp.30078c.
- SAHA, D., GRUNDWALD, D., SICKER, D., 2008. Wireless innovation through software radios. ACM SIGCOMM Computer Communication Review. Volume 39, Issue 1 (January 2009), Pages 62-67.
- WELTE, H. 2010. Harald Welte's blog. [online]. [Accessed 21 April 2009]. Available from World Wide Web: <http://gnumonks.org/~laforge/weblog>
- ZHAO, Y. 2002. Standardization of mobile phone positioning for 3G systems. Communications Magazine, IEEE. Volume 40, Issue 7, pages 108-116.

JOCHEN JÄHNKE

Securing IT-Infrastructure

Gaps between "state-of-the-art" and the reality of daily work

This paper presents in brief the security setup of a small research institution. It considers the necessary amount of money and time spent on IT Security and identifies the challenges such a setup meets in "real life". Finally, it will propose a process to keep abreast of those challenges.

I. Identifying what has to be secured

Ultimatively, what Information Technology is about is the storage, the retrieval, the exchange and the processing of data. Sometimes the focus lies only on one of those tasks, but most of the time there are several of these aspects involved when IT is "at work". This handling of data in one way or the other is performed by special forms of data named "software" on special devices named "hardware". The software is not more than a set of rules and instructions what to do with the data and how to do it. The hardware consists of logical circuits and the support devices like input/ouput and storage, made to enable the software to process the data (*Tanenbaum,* 2003). The hardware can be considererd as a set of rules built into a machine. One could even reduce a computer to an endless roll of toilet paper with a set of predefined rules and still calculate whatever is calculatable as Turing has shown. The computer is a deterministic machine to process data. So at the core of IT lies the data. Hardware and Software are exchangeable in some ways, the information is not. Information or data is what "IT" is all about.

For the purpose of this article I will differ between public, private and confidential data[1]: Public data shall be all data which is published or designated to be published, for example on Websites. Private data is all data which is considered confidential by its owner or by law, e.g. e-mail, customer or employe data. Secret data is confidential data which under no circumstances has to be disclosed, which is critical for the outcome of a project, e.g. the maximum sum one intends to bid at an auction.

---

[1] These classifications for the security of data are similar to the labels for business data seen in http://en.wikipedia.org/wiki/Information_security. For the purpose of this article I neglected the mentioning of the label "sensitive" data. Security classifications are sets of ordinal values. Depending on the organization they might vary as the examples in the wikipedia entry show ("Public, Sensitive, Private, Confidential" vs. "Unclassified, Sensitive But Unclassified, Restricted, Confidential, Secret, Top Secret").

The mission objective of IT-Security is to guarantee the confidentiality, the availability and the integrity of the data[2]. This includes the IT Infrastructure on which this data resides and on which it is transmitted.

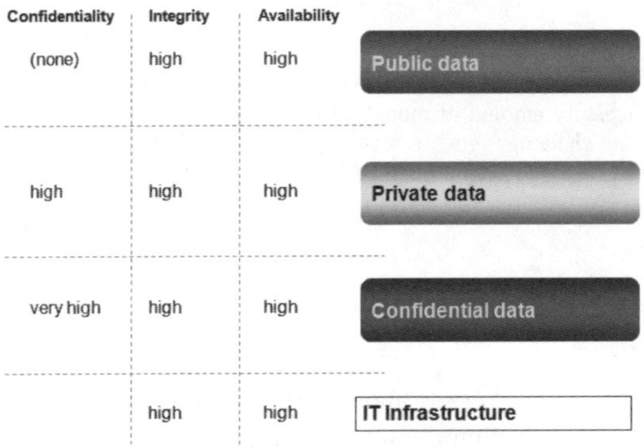

Fig. 1: CIA-requirements with respect to public data, private data, secret data, and IT infrastructure[3]

Figure 1 shows two things: First considering the availability and the integrity there is no big difference between the three types of data. It is not a big mistake to secure everything, even the data which is published on web servers, because the integrity of the data still needs to be high. The availability of private data is often considered as "medium" but only until the day it is lost or not available for a certain amount of time[4]. The confidential or secret data has to be considered separately. Depending on the goal it might take some extraordinary measures to ensure it will be kept secret.

---

[2] See also http://en.wikipedia.org/wiki/Information_security

[3] In this figure there is no label like "medium", either the data integrity and availability should be high or not. There is no "perhaps". The only question is how much money should be invested to reach those goals. The entry for the confidentiality of the IT-Infrastructure was omitted due to the big differences between organizations like for example universities or small firms. While the first might want to puplish their setup to make it usable, the others might want to keep it secret to obscure it to possible attackers.

[4] In our present time the ubiquity of IT creates new dependencies. In former times family pictures where kept in albums, in our time most of the pictures are taken and stored digitally. The loss of this private data is not an option for most people. They are prepared to spend a certain amount of money to save the data. The same applies for communications. In some cases the author knows of, people took the loss of the email system harder than the breakdown of the phone system.

II. The access to data

There are a two major ways to access data: physical access or electronic access. But to consider securing only those two ways would not be comprehensive enough. The data can not only be protected by physical and electronic access restrictions. Physical and electronic access restrictions are only as good as the organizational security measures they are integrated with, as we will see later.

Apart from the technical aspects that are highlighted in this paper, some political decisions stand at the beginning of the security chain: It needs management decisions which data to protect and how to protect it. It takes policies and rules to ensure the protection and periodical audits to assure the correct implementation of those rules. The social element has also to be taken into account: reasons for the adherence to or the neglecting of rules, the gaining of physical or electronic access by social hacking etc. These risks are guarded by the organizational security measures.

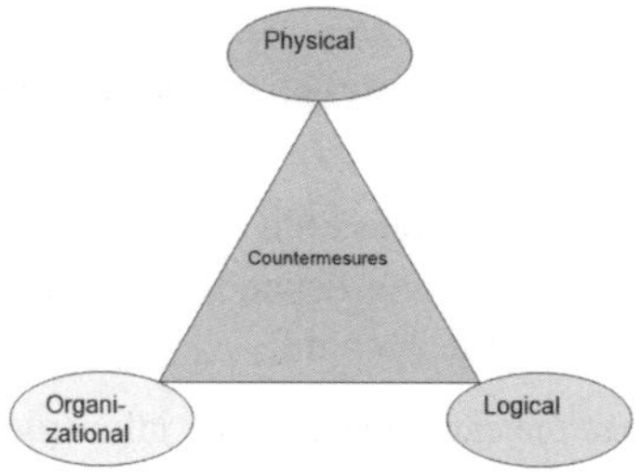

Figure 2: Interdependency of organizational, physical, and logical countermeasures to IT security threats

III. How to protect the data

The biggest danger for data is the loss due to hard- or software failures or desasters like fire etc. Those cases are covered by standard IT-Procedures like backup and the redundant layout of the hardware and are not the focus of this article. This leaves the danger of malicious intend of an intruder, a hacker or some malicious code like a virus etc.

It is safe to assume that a serious attack will try to reach the objective by the easiest way possible. A hypothetical attacker will act economically. Therefore the security of every possible way to gain access to the data has to be considered. By preparing against serious attacks and problems one automatically prepares in most cases against less serious events[5].

The physical, organizational and logical counter measures (see figure 2 above) have to be balanced. There is certainly no big need for a firewall if there are no locks on the door of the server room. And an intrusion detection system is not needed, if old accounts are still active or there are no organizational precautions for example against greed, laziness and stupidity.

IV. An exemplary setup

In the following the security setup of a small institution or business will be described. As an example the setup of the author's institution will be used as a baseline and additional information is given.

A. Physical Security Measures: physical access restrictions

In an ideal setup the building is accessible to guests only during the office hours. Thereby the access inside the building depends on "need" only. Hierarchical considerations should not be taken into account.

The computer room where the electronic security infrastructure and the storage devices reside is only accessible to certain technicians. Outsiders are only allowed inside together with a member of this group and never left alone. The same applies to all other rooms or cabinets with network hardware or, for example, the room with the backup servers. There are also measures to prevent the access to raw data e. g. questionnaires, printouts etc. but this form will not be further considered in this article. Whenever storage hardware is discarded it will be overwritten a few times with random numbers to prevent the restoration of deleted data. Paper will be shredded.

B. Logical Security Measures I: Hardware and Network Layout

In the following the IT-security measures, firewalls and other logical security equipment will be highlighted by following the way a hypothetical attacker from the internet would have to take. On this way the attacker will meet some obstacles that were introduced to secure the company network. (See figure 3 below for an overview).

---

[5] For example, securing against a fire in placing a failover server in a different location is also a countermeasure against the proverbial cleaning woman, who cuts the power of the server while vacuuming the office floor.

1. Packet filter firewall

On the router to the internet resides a so called packet filter firewall. A packet filter firewall controls all the little packets which constitute a network transmission and handles them according to the defined rules. Those rules apply mainly to the source and destination address and the type of service a packet belongs to[6]. A packet filter firewall allows only needed traffic and denies everything else. It could be regarded as a filter or a sieve which filters for source- and destination -address and type of declared data. This firewall is monitored[1] and has one full audit every year.

This kind of firewall technique was state of the art in the late 1990ies. Because it can only judge the type of data by the "label" of the packet it is prone to ignore packets with "forged license plates" because it cannot control the content of the packet. Modern applications – e.g. "skype" – are easily able to "tunnel" traffic through those firewalls. And those firewalls don't recognize malicious content or hijacked connections, as long as they travel on "allowed routes". On the other hand has the management of a packet filter firewall become a basic and easy task. They are cheap, fast and offer a good fundamental protection.

2. Application level firewall, content scanner, intrusion detection system

Because of the development of more sophisticated applications and attacking techniques there is a need of a better control of the content of data packets and streams as they pass through the network. The constant evolution of threats seems to trigger a co-evolution of countermeasures and/or vice versa. To close the gaps left by the packet filter firewall there is a second layer of security behind the router: an application level firewall which controls the traffic for unwanted or malicious content and applications. This firewall scans not only the source and destination of the communications, but also their content and reacts accordingly to the configured rules[7]. For example, if one would like to disallow "skype" or filesharing-applications in a network, the application level firewall

---

[6] One rule to allow the request for web pages to the web server from the internet may look like this: Allow all traffic from every host on the outside network to the web server which belongs to the "http" service.

If this server offers no other service we can disallow all other traffic with a second rule: Deny all other traffic to our web server. Subsequently only packets with the destination http-service (port 80) will reach the server. The Firewall will discard all other packets to this machine.

[7] In comparison to the packet filter firewall the application level firewall has a much bigger task. It can not only look at the address and the type of packet but it has to scan the content of the packet. This needs more operations and therefore more resources in terms of time and processing power. This slows down the performance of the network. To overcome this difficulty there are techniques to reduce the necessary comparisons. One is to scan only certain prominent features of the packets and not all packets or not the whole content. The other technique is to scan for the occurrence of threat patterns, so called signatures. This reduces the resources needed, but depends on an up-to-date signature data base.

has means to block packets of those applications on their way to and from the internet. Another part of this firewall is the content scanner. It scans the content of the incoming and outgoing traffic for viruses and malicious content and blocks it. Also included in the application level gateway may be an intrusion detection system which will monitor the connections and statistically analyze the traffic and connections of the various machines. After a certain time in "learning mode" it can recognize if and when the behavior and the traffic patterns of the monitored machines change and consecutively trigger an alarm[8].

This ideal firewall is monitored and has one full audit every year. From here on inward the network addresses will be translated to hide the structure of the network and to provide more IP-addresses.

3. The network behind the firewall

The network behind the firewall is not without additional security measures. In contrast to the early years of network security it is now well known, that a lot of incidents origin not from the prototypical hacker from some dark corner of the Internet, but from disgruntled employees or a similar source[9] from the inside (*Richardson,* 2007). In the earlier days of the Internet the policy was to guard against intruders from the outside. There has been a shift in paradigm: the policy today may be described by the three maxims

- Everything not explicitly allowed is forbidden
- Encrypt whatever you can without bringing operations to a standstill
- Trust nobody

The DMZ

Behind the application level gateway reside the servers for the public network infrastructure; DNS servers, e-mail gateways, web servers, e-mail servers, etc.. Those servers are monitored and have been hardened. This is the so called demilitarized zone (DMZ). There are no active connections from there to the inside network. All data needed is polled or pushed by connections originating from the inside network.

Further compartmentalization of the company network

Behind the DMZ there will be another packet filter firewall and an application level gateway. The above mentioned review and monitor procedures apply here (and everywhere else in this setup). This firewall has multiple interfaces and divides the network into different levels of security. Every tier has only access to a lower one.

---

[8] The major problem with Intrusion Detection Systems based on statistical analysis is the big number of false positive alarms.

[9] This source may be an already compromised notebook or a server with a virus on it.

Server Farm

On the first layer reside the servers which are necessary for the operation of the next levels, like the DNS-Servers. This is the server farm for the entire intranet.

Public LAN / Wireless LAN

The next level is the lowest layer of security accessible to mere client computers, the public LAN. Here, every Computer and Notebook with a wired connection will be granted access. This network is also the wired endpoint of the WLAN. The WLAN is only accessible via the highest encryption standard and IEEE 802.1x authentication with a valid user name and password.

Inside Network

On the last level resides the inside network. This is the area for confidential data. The network clients of the employees are located here. Also the central file-servers and other servers that provide services for confidential data (e.g. printing) stay in this subnet. No files are stored on the client machines; every file resides only on the server. Stealing a client machine therefore doesn't help in getting the files. Every employee has only access to his or her files and to the files of her group. The server itself is physically secured, hardened and monitored.

Whenever a client is accessing the network-hardware, it is authenticated to the switch via a client certificate via IEEE 802.1X. This is first to prevent rogue clients or unauthorized notebooks from accessing the network and second to deny access from regular clients booted with a live CD loaded with hacker tools.

The secret data

Secret data has to be handled without exposing it to risks. Our hypothetical scientific institute uses a single server with terminal stations for this purpose. Those terminal stations are similar to X-terminals that might be remembered from the good old days. They only power the display and receive only the content of the screen over the network. So wire-tapping will give access only to the content of the particular screen not to the data itself[10]. As long as the server is secure and not accessible from rogue elements, the data won't get out. Needless to say this server and the terminals have no physical connection to other networks, in particular not to the Internet. The data is stored on and retrieved from the server via a monitored Computer in a locked room.

---

[10] Of course, depending on the kind of data processing, the content of the screen might be enough for an attacker. In this examplary case, the hypothetical institute is running statistical analyses which will be published. Only the basic data is confidential. In other circumstances even the I/O units like the terminals might have to be secured.

The monitoring network

There is another part of the network that hasn't been discussed yet. It is only accessible from the inside network and there is a packet filter firewall to secure it. Behind this firewall the management interfaces of the servers, the UPS[11], the computers for the building automation and all other devices with a web-interface and a functionality which is sensitive from a security point of view are located. This network is only accessible through some management stations. This setup prevents for example denial of service attacks by shutting down a server or cut the whole power supply of the building.

Providing Access to Employees abroad

This of course is only the local view. The researchers working outside the institution need sometimes to have access to the inside network to use the resources offered there. This is accomplished via a SSL-gateway[12]. Full access is only granted to a small group of people. The authentication is guarded not only with a username and a password, but with extra security with a pin number and a one-time password from a security token.

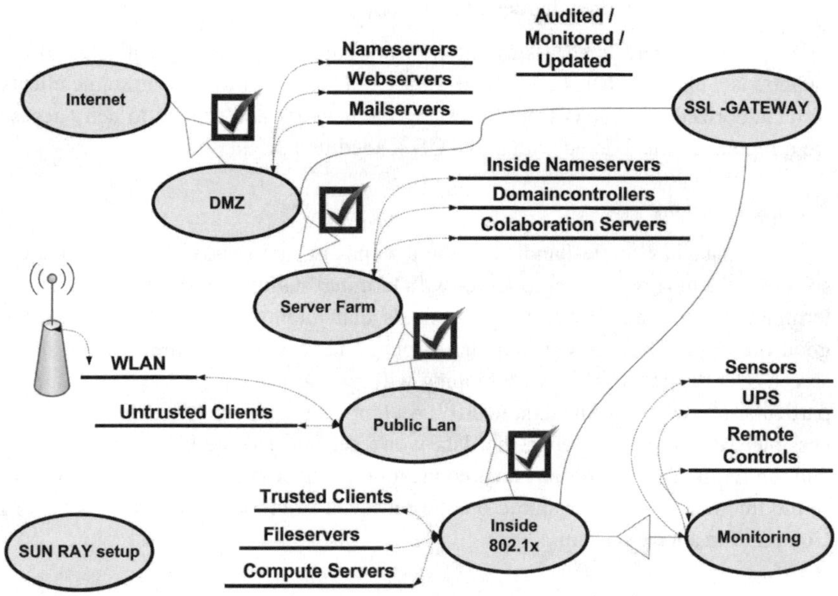

Figure 3: Overview on the setup

11 UPS=Uninterruptable Power Supply

12 SSL=Secure Socket Layer; a encrypted protocol for Web-applications

This is the security setup of the physical network. In the following the logical aspects of this setup will be discussed in further detail.

C. Logical Security Measures II: Protocol, encryption and Software

1. Protocol, encryption and authentication aspects

If possible encrypted protocols are chosen over plain text. Only personalized logins are allowed. Authenticated sessions are chosen over anonymous ones. Private data on mobile devices has to be encrypted. Questionnaires and scientific data is anonymized or adequately protected.

2. Software-Aspects

There is a lot of software installed specifically for security reasons. I will only mention a few.

On each application level gateway content scanners constantly examine the in- and outgoing data, as already mentioned above. On each client machine no code is allowed to run without clearance from the virus engine. No e-mail reaches or leaves the institute without being checked by at least two virus scanners. All threat signatures are constantly kept up to date. All software is constantly updated wherever it is possible. If it is feasible, automatic functions are used. The updates are monitored.

D. Organizational and Procedural Security Measures

The Organizational Security Measures are the third column on which the IT-Security resides. They define policies and workflows to strengthen the organizational and procedural backbone of the whole security setup. Organizational Security is based on management decisions. Those management decisions are reviewed after a certain period of time.

1. Security Policy

There is a written security policy. This defines the goals and the intentions of the Organization in regard towards (IT)-Security. The Security Policy is defined by the management. Everything else is build around it.

2. User Policy

There is a written user policy. Everybody who wants an account for the computers has to sign it. There are procedures implemented for the management of these accounts. This defines and ensures the responsible use of the IT-Systems and names sanctions for missuse.

3. Incident Management Policy

There is a written incident management policy. Every employee on a critical position knows the rules. There is a code of conduct for a lot of procedures around the IT. This ensures coordinated and rational actions in the case of disaster, attacks or else.

4. Documentation

Everything is documented. The documentation is up to date and revised once a year. This is primarily to enable every person to substitute absent co-workers and secondarily to give transparency to procedures. The documentation is reviewed and updated regularily.

5. Training

The staff of the organization is regularily trained in their role and in awareness regarding security. This ensures everybody knows the rules and is a necessary precaution against some attacks (e.g. social hacking).

E. Costs

This is the whole IT security setup of our hypothetical institute[13]. It costs approximately fifty thousand Euros per year[14]. This sum includes all three types of security measures, hardware, software, organization and manpower. It is around fifteen percent of the total amount annually spend on IT and IT-Infrastructure (including manpower).

V. Reality

Unfortunately reality often looks different. The following section highlights some aspect of the authors experience with real life security setups, some of them found in the research institution he works at.

---

[13] To give some more figures, this applies to a research institute with 200 client computers, 30 servers, and about 50 plus networked devices. There are 250 users on the network and 150 mailusers.

[14] These figures are based on recent internal research. They correspond well with other findings.

A. Reality and physical security measures

Some people very high in the hierarchy have full physical access to servers and network hardware; some people very low in the hierarchy[15] have it also. This compromises the "need only" directive. Those people are not part of the IT-Staff and most of the time not briefed on the particulars of a server room or the organizational security measures like the "four-eyes-principle". Even well meant actions can lead to a disaster, e.g. throwing the wrong switch or granting people access without the right clearance. Those security risks can easily be fixed with a review of access policy and some changed locks. Some of the staff will be trained in security awareness and procedures.

B. Reality and logical security measures: hardware and network layout

There are a few servers with collaboration tools with a certain amount of private data in the DMZ. This is against the rule "no private data in the DMZ". As the DMZ is a zone with a low security level, the data there is not as secure as it might need to be. As a remedy this data could be encrypted. At least, the risks should be communicated to the users.

Some of the above mentioned hardware simply does not exist. The application level gateways for example haven't yet been bought, because of a lack of funding. This setup is not state of the art and prone to attacks with second or third generation hacking techniques, as discussed in B.2. Without an application level firewall even the features of standard software might pose a risk[16]. It has to be decided wether this complies with the security policy. If not, either the policy has to be changed or the funding. There might be other technical solutions to this problem[17].

Due to a lack of resources in personel or to a momentarily interference with higher priorities, some server, devices or services are not monitored. As a direct consequence there is no alarm if such a service etc. is malfunctioning. Constant reviews and scans of the company network might reveal those holes and they could be fixed.

---

[15] There are a lot of stories floating around of people in overalls entering security zones without being questioned. Moreover, the cleaning staff, the janitor and the company technician often have master keys for every room in the building.

[16] E.g.: skype or other colaboration software comes with file sharing tools wich might be used to give data access to outsiders.

[17] E.g. a virus scanner might be used to ban certain applications. If the executable file of the application is tagged as a virus the scan engine will refuse to start the application.

C. Reality and organizational security measures

The third pillar of IT-Security is in the authors experience commonly the weakest in real setups. Organizational IT-Security is historically speaking also the youngest[18] of the three aspects of IT-Security. While the general professionalization of the IT has reached a very high degree organizational security has emerged only recently and is frequently not yet fully developed. In the following some common issues will be named.

There is no Security Policy. Management hasn't yet come around to formulate one. Without this all other measures are without a strong foundation and the staff acts without a real backing. Needless to say this will hamper productivity and lead to other problems as we will see below.

Also there is often no Incident Management Policy to speak of, just a few thoughts and templates in the head of the IT professionels. If disaster strickes and the right personel is not available, then there will be very likely also no organized answer to the problem. Therefore possible incidents should be defined and possible actions planned accordingly.

There seems not to be enough time to implement and follow all procedures. Audits are postponed or sometimes neglected due a certain lack of resources. Some procedures haven't yet been implemented. Either there are too much procedures or to less resources. Fixing this is depending on management decisions.

There often are scant measures against insiders with malicious intend. More than thirty percent of the observed perpetrations seem to originate from inside. Depending on the type of organization and the local IT Security Policy it seems appropriate to do something about this. Policies for this have to be worked out and implemented.

Not every client computer is managed by the IT Department; some people have administrator privileges on their machine or on a server. Sometimes they need those privileges to do their work. Sometimes it might be or become necessary. Sometimes they only think it is necessary. Those client machines are a constant threat to the overall setup. Unwittingly those people may install malicious software and so compromise the whole setup of firewalls, because their machines are already in the internal network. In most cases a few considerations could ensure the implementation of a "need only" policy. Or there might be some other solution to keep this threat under control, like regular scans of those machines or an application scanner like mentioned in footnote 17.

And the biggest difference between state of the art and real life: Of course, NOT everything is documented. This is a very common issue. As a direct consequence

---

[18] Physical security has doubtless a very long history. Technical IT-Security is also well matured.

only the informed person can act accordingly. If this person is not available, direct action might be difficult, due to an unnessesary lack of information. This issue has to be taken care of also. The best way is to analyse the nessesary amount of documentation and schedule regular audits.

VI. Conclusion

The constant change in threats because of the coevolution of attacks and defences and the rapid development of IT will surely not stop. To keep ahead of these developments a constant change of IT-Security is unavoidable.

The main problem as we have seen lies not in the areas of physical or technical security. Those areas are well understood and can be covered provided the necessary resources exist or are available. The difficulties arise in the third area, the organizational security. Some foundation stones like the IT-Security Policy might be missing and nessesary procedures haven't yet been implemented. An IT-Security Process has to be established and the procedure has to be repeated in iterations:

- The management has to agree about security measures. There should be an IT-Security Policy.
- The issues have to be named. Hierarchical considerations have to be left out.
- The whole system has to be regarded. Technical, social and psychological components have to be considered.
- Security costs money. For zero money you will get zero security.
- Repeat this process regularily. Revise where ever nessesarry.

References

- RICHARDSON, R., CSI Computer Crime and Security Survey 2007 [online]. Available from World Wide Web: http://www.gocsi.com.
- SANS, 2010. Outline for a Successful Security Program [online]. [Accessed 30 June 2010]. Available from World Wide Web: http://www.sans.org/reading_room/whitepapers/basics/outline-successful-security-program_1208.
- TANENBAUM, A.S. Computer networks. Upper Saddle River, N.J., 2003.
- WIKIPEDIA, 2010. Information Security [online]. [Accessed 30 June 2010]. Available from World Wide Web: http://en.wikipedia.org/wiki/Information_security.

Ramona Rantala

Cybercrime against Businesses

> Everyone knows that cybercrime and other computer incidents are a growing problem. But no one really knows how large, how fast it's growing, or where the problems are concentrated. And you can't manage what you can't measure. The more we know about the extent of cybercrime, the better we'll all be able to combat it.
>
> *Paul Kurtz*
> Executive Director (then)
> Computer Security Industry Alliance

Those responsible for computer security, including businesses providing computer security hardware, software, and services; law enforcement; and U.S. federal agencies recognize the need for reliable cybercrime data. Required information includes the nature and prevalence of computer security incidents, monetary losses and system downtime caused by such incidents, types of offenders, reporting incidents to authorities, and best security practices. In response to the need for reliable data in these areas, the Bureau of Justice Statistics developed the National Computer Security Survey.

I. Existing Data Inadequate

At the time the survey was developed, the information that existed on computer security was scattered, incomplete, or inextricably merged with other information.

The Federal Trade Commission (FTC) compiles data reported to them by consumers who were victims of identity theft. The Bureau of Justice Statistics collects data on identity theft from a sample of 76,000 households through the National Crime Victimization Survey (NCVS). Both the FTC and the NCVS measure the number of victims of identity theft and the resulting losses. However, neither of these data collections differentiates whether these crimes occurred through e-commerce or other computer transactions, or by more traditional means such as a stolen credit card.

The National Prosecutors Survey collects data on which of the nation's 2,300 state prosecutorial offices litigate computer-related crimes, and what type of charges are filed. The survey does not quantify the number of cases or type of victim (e.g., individual persons or businesses).

The Federal Justice Statistics Program contains information on federal cases of crimes which may be computer-related. However, as with the FTC and NCVS data, cybercrimes are not differentiated from crimes committed through other means.

The Federal Bureau of Investigation collects data from state and local law enforcement agencies, including whether a computer was used in the commission of a crime. Unfortunately, this information is ambiguous for many types of crime. For example, the data document instances in which a computer is used in the commission of a homicide. Does this mean the victim met the offender online? Or that the offender stalked the victim via e-mail and chat rooms? Or does it mean the offender literally killed the victim by, say, hitting them on the head with a laptop? Similar ambiguities exist for robbery and theft. Does the use of a computer in these crimes mean the crime was researched or set-up via computer? Or simply that the stolen property included a computer?

One other source of cybercrime data comes from private data collections, one conducted by the Computer Security Institute (CSI), the other conducted by CSO, an online resource for Chief Security Officers. The CSI Computer Crime and Security Survey is the longest standing survey of its type. However, rather than employing scientific probability sampling methods, CSI uses a sample of convenience – the 5,000 members of the Institute. This, coupled with response rates that range from 7% to 15% (about 300 to 600 respondents), means that the findings cannot be used to form a reliable estimate of what is happening within the nation's millions of businesses. With 880 respondents, the CSO survey has similar methodological issues.

II. Developing New Measures of Cybercrime

These data collections provided a springboard for a more focused effort related to cybercrime. The scope of this study is limited to 1) businesses and 2) victimizations. Information on suspected, alleged or confirmed perpetrations of a cybercrime by a business or any of its employees was not requested and is out-of-scope of this study. What we needed to know included –

- Is crime increasing or just shifting from physical to electronic means?
- What businesses are the victims of cybercrime?
- What is the impact of cybercrime?
- Are cybercrime incidents reported to authorities? If not, why not?
- What are the most vulnerable points of computer systems?
- Which security technologies, measures, and practices are most effective?

As the NIBRS data aptly illustrates, that the term cybercrime is ambiguous. At its broadest, it can mean any crime in which a computer or an electronic device is involved in some way. For our purposes, *cybercrime* is defined as an incident in which a computer or network is the target of an attack or is used to commit a crime. It is divided into three areas: cyber attacks, cyber theft, and other computer security incidents.

Cyber attacks include incidents in which the all or part of the computer system is the target. The goal is often to disrupt business. Common types of cyber attacks include

- Computer viruses, worms, Trojan horses
- Denial of service
- Electronic vandalism or sabotage

Cyber theft, incidents in which a computer was used to illegally obtain money, goods, or services. Common types of cyber theft include

- Embezzlement
- Fraud
- Theft of intellectual property
- Theft of personal or financial data

Other computer security incidents include incidents that do not fit the general definitions of cyber attack or cyber theft. Common types of other computer security incidents include

- Spyware, adware, other malware
- Phishing, spoofing
- Hacking
- Pinging, scanning, sniffing
- Theft of other information

III. Computer Security Survey Pilot Study

Prior to launching the national survey, the Bureau of Justice Statistics conducted a pre-test, the Computer Security Survey Pilot Study. In partnership with the U.S. Census Bureau, the pilot study was a feasibility test on collecting sensitive cyber security data from U. S. businesses. The goal was to determine whether the data were reportable and if companies would participate.

Development of the pilot study questionnaire employed extensive testing of questions with 69 companies operating in 14 different industries across the United States. By the end of 2002, the questionnaire was finalized. The reference (reporting) period was calendar year 2001. Of the 500 companies that received the survey (including a series of follow-ups), 42% responded. The vast majority of these responding companies (95%) used computers.

The companies that did not respond were contacted to determine their reasons for non-response. Of the 118 companies providing reasons, 82% said they participated only in mandatory surveys, 42% didn't have time, 17% cited concerns with their responses being kept confidential, and 14% said the data to answer the cybercrime questions were not available. (Note: multiple reasons could be provided.) Overall, the feasibility test results indicated that data were reportable. However, getting companies to participate in a voluntary survey would be problematic. The full report, *Cybercrime against Businesses, 2001 Pilot Study*, is available online (Rantala, 2004).

IV. National Computer Security Survey

A. Presidential directive

In 2003, the Department of Justice was directed to collect better data about victims of cybercrime.

The National Strategy to Secure Cyberspace, Priority II: A National Cyberspace Security Threat and Vulnerability Reduction Program:

"DOJ and other appropriate agencies will develop and implement efforts to reduce cyber attacks and cyber threats through . . . developing better data about victims of cybercrime and intrusions in order to understand the scope of the problem and to be able to track changes over time." (A/R 2-1)

The Bureau of Justice Statistics formed partnerships with other components within the U.S. Department of Justice: the Computer Crime and Intellectual Property Section and the FBI's Cyber Security Squad. Partnerships were also formed with the U.S. Department of Homeland Security: the National Cyber Security Division and the U.S. Secret Service. Public and private organizations endorsed the survey.

B. Rigorous testing

A private sector data collection organization and various computer security experts were consulted to modify the pilot test survey instrument. Questions measuring number of virus infections, monetary loss, and system downtime were refined, new types of computer security technology and using third party computer security contractors were included. The revised questionnaire underwent rigorous cognitive testing. Both questionnaires together were tested on nearly100 companies. More emphasis was placed on confidentiality of responses. Respondents were informed that results would be published in summary form in such a way as individual companies would not be identifiable. Businesses were also assured that the raw data would not be publicly available.

C. Sample design

The NCSS used a carefully constructed probability sample design. The scope of the survey was limited to businesses owned and operated in the United States. Governmental organizations, educational institutions, and private households were not included in the sample. Non-employers, that is, businesses owned and operated by a single individual or family, were also excluded based on the difficulty in obtaining an accurate list of such businesses. There were approximately 7.3 million businesses in the scope of the survey.

The sampling frame, Dun and Bradstreet, was the most comprehensive list of businesses available to the public at the time. This listing was stratified by risk level, type of industry, and size of company. Companies operating in industries determined to be part of the U.S. critical infrastructure industries were assigned the highest risk level. The remaining industries assigned risk levels depending on the perceived likelihood of a cyber security incident or the perceived risk of loss if they were to victim of a cyber incident (Table 1). A sample size of 36,000 companies was determined sufficient to detect, over time, a 2.5% change in cybercrime rates within a 90% confidence interval.

Critical Infrastructure	High Risk
Agriculture	Manufacturing, durable
Chemical and drug mfg	Manufacturing, non-durable goods
Computer system design	Motion picture and sound recording
Finance	Retail
Health care	Scientific research and development
Internet service providers	Wholesale
Petroleum mining and manufacturing	
Publications and broadcasting	
Real estate	
Telecommunications	
Transportation and pipelines	
Utilities	

Table 1: National Computer Security Survey sample design, industry by risk level

Moderate risk	Low risk
Accounting	Accomodations
Advertising	Administrative support
Architecture and engineering	Arts & entertainment
Business and technical schools	Construction
Insurance	Food services
Legal services	Forestry, fishing, and hunting
	Management of companies
	Mining
	Rental services
	Social services
	Other services
	Warehousing

Table 1 cont'd: National Computer Security Survey sample design, industry by risk level

D. Maximizing response rates

As illustrated by the 2001 pilot test, further measures would have to be employed to increase the survey's response rate. Making the survey mandatory would have been the most effective measure. Current legislation did not appear to support justifying a mandatory survey. To add new legislation of this type generally takes an act of Congress, which was not an option at the time.

Many other measures could be taken. The first, as mentioned above, was stressing the confidentiality of the survey. Publicity was also an effective tool. The Department of Justice issued a press release announcing the survey (link), and urging companies to participate. Endorsements from industry leaders, computer security experts, business and trade associations, and others were obtained. These organizations allowed their names to be listed as endorsers, and also assisted in publicizing the survey and encouraged their constituents to participate if selected in the sample. A project website was established (http://bjs.ojp.usdoj.gov/index.cfm?ty=tp&tid=324). It included background information about the survey, DOJ, DHS, and the data collectors. The project website also discussed the importance of the survey and benefits of solid data for government and industry. It provided links to an online (password protected) survey, Frequently Asked Questions, and contact information.

The preceding methodology and subsequent findings are available online in the BJS Special Report, *Cybercrime against Businesses, 2005* (Rantala, 2008).

V. NCSS Response Rates

Response to the survey varied by company size and industry. Large companies were more likely to respond to the survey (27% of companies sampled) compared to small companies (18%), with a 23% response rate overall (Table 2). Risk level did not appear to be a factor in response rates.

Deaggregating the number of employee groups shows that companies with 2-9 employees had the lowest response (15%).

	Number of businesses			Response
Number of employees	Universe	Sample	Response	rate
All businesses	7,278,109	35,596	8,079	23 %
2 to 24	6,771,026	11,479	2,056	18
25 to 99	396,355	5,601	1,236	22
100 to 999	98,585	11,472	2,894	25
1,000 or more	12,143	7,044	1,893	27

Table 2: NCSS Universe, responses, and response rate

Within this group of companies with 2-9 employees, the industries with the lowest response rates included Recording (7%), Accommodations (8%), and Food Services (10%). Companies with 5,000 to 9,999 employees had the highest response rates (32.7%). Within this size group, the industries with the highest rates included Social Services (100%), Accounting (75%), and 7 other industries with 50% or more companies responding.

Of the 8,079 businesses responding, 3% did not have computers. These businesses operated mainly in the industries of Agriculture (18% did not have computers), Forestry, Fishing and Hunting (12%), Food Services (12%), and Warehousing (10%). Overall, 7,818 respondents did have computers. All (100%) of the responding Computer System Design, Finance, Health Care, Internet Service Providers, Publications and Broadcasting, Telecommunications, Accounting, and Insurance companies used computers.

Response rates varied by type of industry. Utility companies had the highest response rate (37%), followed by Social Services (33%), and Health Care (29%, see figure1). The Recording Industries (14%), Accommodations (14%), and Telecommunications (16%) had the lowest response rates.

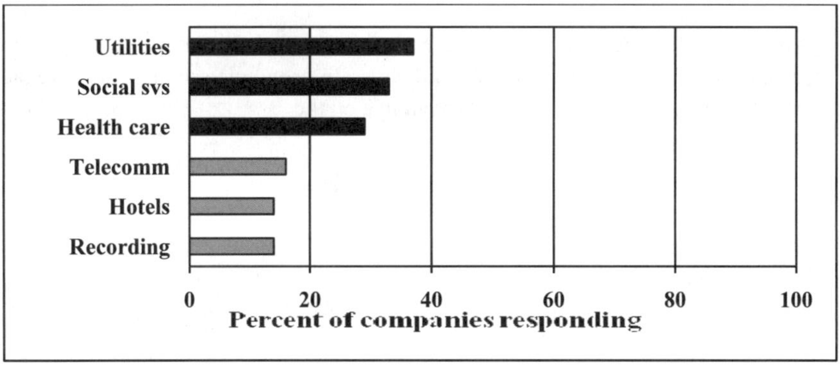

Figure 1: Highest and Lowest Response Rates, by Economic Sector, 2005

VI. Detection of Cybercrime

Overall, 67% of respondents detected at least one computer security incident (Table 3). Again, detection varied with size of company. A higher percentage of larger companies (82%) detected computer security incidents compared to 50% of the smallest companies. Questions remained. How representative were these data? Could they be used to compute national estimates? The raw percentages of businesses detecting cybercrime were compared to weighted percentages. Within each size category, the weighted estimates were no more than four percentage points lower than the raw data. The standard errors ranged from 1.3% to 2.7%, suggesting the data might produce reliable national estimates, controlling for size of company. This would be the case only if the non-respondents detection was the same as those responding to the survey. However, there was insufficient information to determine this. For this reason and because the audience of this conference was largely IT practitioners, the analysis of weighted estimates and confidence intervals is presented but not discussed in depth in this paper.

	Response rate		Percent of businesses detecting cybercrime		
Number of employees	Overall	Item	Unw eighted	Weighted	Standard Error
All businesses	23 %	21 %	67 %	48 %	2.5 %
2 to 24	18	15	50	46	2.7
25 to 99	22	21	59	57	2.1
100 to 999	25	25	70	67	1.4
1,000 or more	27	26	82	80	1.3

Table 3: Response and Detection of Cybercrime, by Company Size, 2005

Although using the data to produce national estimates is not advised, the data represent more than 8,000 businesses and cover 36 economic sectors. They are the most reliable and comprehensive data available on the

- Nature of computer security incidents
- Prevalence by industry and type of incident
- Monetary losses
- Downtime
- Types of offenders
- Reporting incidents to authorities
- Vulnerabilities leading to breaches

	Response rate		Percent of businesses detecting		
Industry	Overall	Item	Unw eighted	Weighted	Standard Error
All industries	23 %	21 %	67 %	48 %	2.5 %
Utilities	37	36	64	43	4.8
Social services	33	31	66	55	9.6
Health care	29	28	67	56	8
Telecommunication	16	16	82	67	10.1
Accommodations	14	13	60	23	7.2
Recording Industry	14	13	67	56	13.7

Table 4: Detection of cybercrime in industries with the highest and lowest response rates, 2005

Of responding Utility companies, 64% detected cybercrime (Table 4). Weighted values estimate that 43% of all Utility companies detected cybercrime in 2005. With the highest precision, the true proportion of Utility companies detecting cybercrime is between 33% and 53%.[1] The estimate is less precise for all other industries. For example, while 82% of responding Telecommunication companies detected at least one cybercrime in 2005, the true proportion of all Telecommunication companies detecting at least one cybercrime is estimated to be between 47% and 87%. The Recording industry showed the least precision. The true proportion of Recording companies detecting cybercrime is estimated to be between 29% and 83%.

VII. Monetary Losses

About half of responding companies lost a total of $1,000 to $9,000 from cybercrime in 2005 (Figure 2). About 10% of companies detecting cybercrime suffered no monetary losses, and 12% sustained losses of $100,000 or more. Weighted estimates suggest that the true proportion of companies sustaining no losses is between 14% and 30%, and the true proportion of those losing from $10,000 to $99,000 is between 6% and 12%.

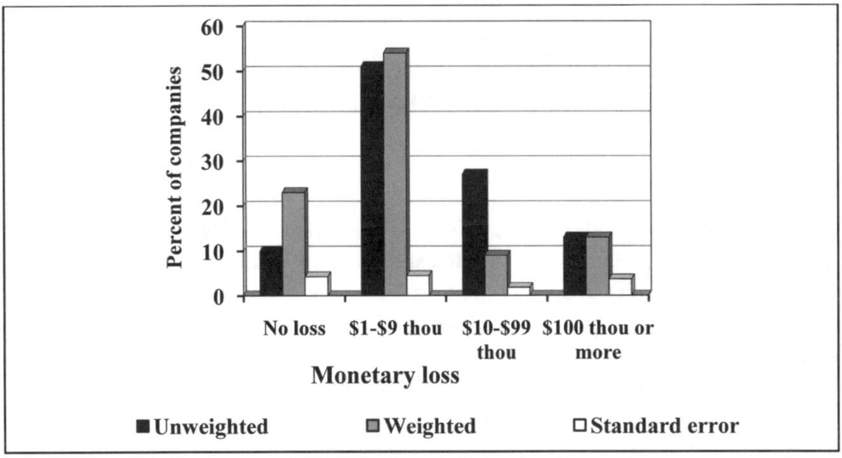

Figure 2: Monetary Losses from Cybercrime, 2005

Companies sustained the greatest losses from cyber theft. Two-thirds of responding companies reported losses of $10,000 or more, and nearly one-third had losses

[1] For p< .05; a 95% confidence interval is used throughout this paper.

of $100,000 or more (Figure 3). But the standard errors are higher for cyber theft compared to overall cybercrime, so that the true proportion of companies sustaining cyber theft losses of $100,000 or more is between 16% and 68%.

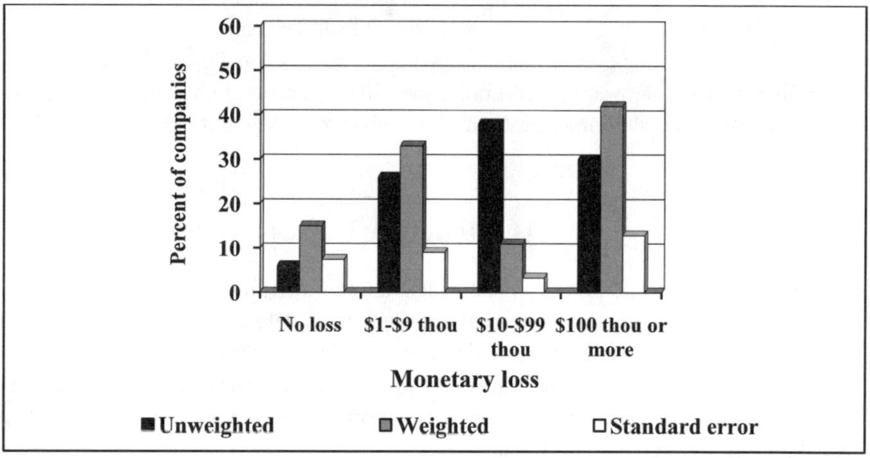

Figure 3: Monetary Losses from Cyber Theft, 2005

VIII. Suspected Cybercrime Offenders

Differences between cyber attacks and cyber theft were also observed when looking at types of suspected cybercrime offenders. When responding companies had some information about who may have perpetrated a cyber attack, 74% of the time it was someone external to the attacked company (Table 5). On the other hand, the suspected offender of a cyber theft was someone internal to or closely affiliated with the company for 74% of respondents who had information on the perpetrator. While this has been common belief supported by anecdotal evidence, the NCSS has provided the first empirical data to support this hypothesis.

	Percent of businesses reporting cyber theft		
Type of incident and offender	Unweighted	Weighted	Standard Error
Cyber attack offender			
Insider	27 %	12 %	3.0 %
Outsider	74	81	3.8
Cyber theft offender			
Insider	74 %	49 %	3.1 %
Outsider	32	49	3.4

Table 5: Suspected cyber offenders, 2005

IX. Reporting Cybercrime to Authorities

The overall reporting of cybercrime to authorities did not differ much by type of crime. However, to whom the crime was reported did vary by whether the crime was a cyber attack or cyber theft. More than 80% of respondents detecting some type of cyber attack reported an attack to someone within their company, 14% reported an attack to another organization such as their internet service provider, 6% reported an attack to law enforcement authorities, and 14% did not report cyber attacks to anyone (Table 6).

	Percent of businesses reporting cyber attacks		
Cyber attack was reported—	Unweighted	Weighted	Standard Error
Somewhere	86 %	78 %	2.4 %
Within the company	81	73	2.6
To another organization	14	17	2.1
To law enforcement	6	3	1.1

Table 6: Reporting cyber attacks, 2005

For responding companies victimized by cyber theft, however, 92% reported a theft to someone: 56% reported to law enforcement authorities, 46% reported within the company, and 9% reported a cyber theft to another organization (Table 7).

	Percent of businesses reporting cyber theft		
Cyber attack was reported—	Unweighted	Weighted	Standard Error
Somewhere	92 %	79 %	8.0 %
Within the company	46	33	6.5
To another organization	9	7	2.3
To law enforcement	56	44	7.8

Table 7: Reporting cyber theft, 2005

These findings are expected, given the high economic loss often associated with cyber theft, and that many perpetrators are known to the company. Companies indicated that many cyber attacks went unreported or reported within the company only because the victimized companies did not think to report it outside the company or decided it was not worth reporting. Reasons for this include the lower monetary loss associated with cyber attacks and the difficulty in identifying or tracking down the perpetrator.

X. Future Plans and Challenges

Many U.S. Federal agencies recognize the value of a data collection such as the National Computer Security Survey (NCSS). The need for reliable information such as that provided by NCSS is also acknowledged. However, the difficulties of effectively gathering this information have not gone unnoticed. And while the

NCSS is the best effort to date for collecting the needed data, many challenges must be overcome if sufficient response rates are to be achieved.

The NCSS is a voluntary survey. In the follow-up conducted with non-respondents during the earlier pilot study, the vast majority of companies indicated that they participate in mandatory surveys only. There are Federal regulations governing what type of survey can be mandatory, and more research needs to be conducted to determine if the NCSS fits the criteria.

The mandatory vs. voluntary nature of the survey is particularly crucial for the NCSS because of the sensitivity of the data requested. The survey asks the company's Chief Information Officer or Information Technology Manager where they failed and what it cost the company. It is understandable that many companies would be reluctant to release this type of information to an outsider.

Non-response is one data quality issue. There are others as well. Even for those companies that do respond, there are challenges with the reported data. One obstacle to accurately measuring the prevalence of cybercrime is that companies cannot report what they did not detect. For example, many companies have a policy that if an employee's PC crashes, rather than take the time to determine the cause, the hard drive is simply reformatted and software reloaded. If all data and documents are stored on the company network, this method is very efficient and nothing is lost. What is lost, however, is an accurate account of virus infections and the resulting downtime and monetary losses for companies with these practices.

Another obstacle is that even the best definitions can be ambiguous. For example, as the technological capabilities of some mobile phones and Personal Digital Assistants (PDAs) increase, they may or may not be part of a company's computer network. Also, the definitions of various types of cybercrime overlap, so it may not always clear to a respondent how to categorize a particular incident, or how to count single vs. multiple incidents for virus infections. Another ambiguity is caused by the outsourcing of IT functions. Businesses that outsource some or all of their computer security may not be able to provide the information to us. More questions could be added to obtain some of these details. This would increase the utility of the data, but it would also increase the burden on respondents.

A related challenge is the speed with which technology develops. Technology evolves very quickly, and it takes time to conduct a data collection. The result is that by the time the questionnaire has been finalized and sent out, the technology has already changed or new issues in computer security have emerged. The effect is similar to that of trying to hit a moving target.

None of these challenges are insurmountable. But careful consideration must be given to dealing with each one of them. For more details, findings, and methodology, see *Rantala* (2008).

References

- RANTALA, R. 2004. Cybercrime against Businesses: Pilot Test Results, 2001 Computer Security Survey. Available from World Wide Web: <http://bjs.ojp.usdoj.gov/index.cfm?ty=pbdetail&iid=770>.
- RANTALA, R. 2008. Cybercrime against Businesses, 2005. Available from World Wide Web: <http://bjs.ojp.usdoj.gov/index.cfm?ty=pbdetail&iid=769>.

David Wall

THE ORGANIZATION OF CYBERCRIME AND ORGANIZED CYBERCRIME

It will be argued in this article that the debate over organised crime online can only be advanced by looking at the ways that crime is organised online. The article will therefore begin by briefly outlining the current debate over organised crime online and drawing upon known examples of the organisation of cybercrime. In order to illustrate how 'true' cybercrimes – those wholly mediated by the internet – are being organised, a detailed analysis of scareware, a relatively new form of malicious software, will follow. The article will show that the organisation of crime online, when it involves 'true' cybercrimes does not lend itself to traditional 'Mafia-type' command and control analogies; furthermore, it is arguable that the networked technologies that facilitate cybercrime could/ would actually oppose attempts to impose control over them. Instead, it will be argued that the organisation of crime online follows a different logic, an observation which has implications both for law enforcement as well as cybercrime prevention because it is a logic that lends itself to a relativist rather than absolutist conceptualisation of cybercrime. In other words, we have to accept that, by its very nature; cybercrime characteristically evolves in order to evade attempts to control it and therefore can never be eradicated; only managed.

The debate over organised cybercrime and the internet is likely to run and run because it is highly emotive and newsworthy, especially as commentators continue to resort to convenient stereotypes of traditional-hierarchical organised crime groups or 'Mafias' when there is a dearth of facts. This simplification of the relationship between organised crime and the internet has a powerful cultural logic, especially as the fraud statistics clearly show that the internet is increasingly being used by fraudsters to steal large amounts of money from innocent victims. The main challenge, however, for policy makers and practitioners is to identify exactly who the fraudsters are and how they are organised because, despite the hyperbole, comparatively little is known about them or how they are organised. Until more research is undertaken to understand the nature of organised crime online then the existing assumptions will carry the day. Whilst the mythology of organised crime remains intact, then so does the potential for misshapen public demands for security, distortions in the formation of policy and ultimately the mis-allocation of resources.

It will be argued in this article that the debate over organised crime online can only be advanced by looking at the ways that crime is organised online. The article will therefore begin by briefly outlining the current debate over organised crime online and drawing upon known examples of the organisation of cybercrime. In order to illustrate how 'true' cybercrimes – those wholly mediated by the internet –

are being organised, a detailed analysis of scareware, a relatively new form of malicious software, will follow. The article will show that the organisation of crime online, when it involves 'true' cybercrimes (Wall, 2007: 47) does not lend itself to traditional 'Mafia-type' command and control analogies; furthermore, it is arguable that the networked technologies that facilitate cybercrime could/ would actually oppose attempts to impose control over them. Instead, it will be argued that the organisation of crime online follows a different logic, an observation which has implications both for law enforcement as well as cybercrime prevention because it is a logic that lends itself to a relativist rather than absolutist conceptualisation of cybercrime. In other words, we have to accept that, by its very nature; cybercrime characteristically evolves in order to evade attempts to control it and therefore can never be eradicated; only managed.

I. Deconstructing the organised crime debate

In her study of organised criminal activity on the internet, Susan Brenner predicted that organised cybercrime would most likely manifest itself in 'transient, lateral and fluid' forms, as networks of criminals (Brenner 2002, p. 1) rather than replicate the 'gang' and hierarchical American 'Mafia' models of organised criminal activity found offline in the terrestrial world. This is mainly because (offline or kinetic/ physical) crime organisations have evolved largely in response to real world opportunities and constraints that are largely absent in cyberspace. In support of Brenner's 2002 prediction, there have since been a number of examples of the emergence of new forms of online criminal organisation, but they differ greatly from the command and control mafia model. The finding in 2004 by a German Magazine *C'T*, for example, that virus writers had been selling the IP addresses of computers infected with their remote administration Trojans to spammers (C'T 2004) was significant because it was some of the first published evidence of botnets (following the botnet explosion in 2003/04). Another example arose in June 2005 when the NISCC (National Infrastructure Security Coordination Centre) warned users about 'a highly sophisticated high-tech gang' reputed to be located in the far-East using various distributed means, including botnets, to infect sensitive computer systems to steal government and business secrets (NISCC 2005; Warren 2005).

A further example arose from 'Operation Firewall' which led to the investigation and prosecution of 'shadowcrew', an international identity theft network which hosted online forums that shared information about stealing, trading and selling personal information that could be used to commit frauds. Thc various reports of the investigation and prosecution illustrate how different the groups were in terms of their networked organisation. The, then, head of e-crime at the Serious Organised Crime Agency (SOCA) observed that the Shadowcrew worked 'remotely, without ever needing to meet', which is 'typical of how the new e-crime networks operate compared to the old-style "top down" organised crime groups' (Rodgers 2007). These groups have a very detailed division of labour with specific skill sets rather than the 'usual pyramid structure'. One person would provide the documents, 'another would buy credit card details, another would create identities while another would provide the drop address' (Rodgers 2007). Together these examples, and also those of other known cybercrime gangs operating between 2000-2010 listed in Figure 1, illustrate the relatively new forms of networked criminal organisation that depart from traditional thinking about hierarchically organised crime. Although these gangs specialised in a range of different offences, they displayed similar forms of organisation. Word length does not allow for in-depth analysis of each, but briefly, they display common characteristics in that they are fairly ephemeral and amorphous in terms of organisation and flex according to demands and opportunities of the day. They also seem to be mostly self-contained and very like small cottage-industries in structure. They can be driven by an individual or by a very small group, but not always, because the organising principle can also be a common idea. Just because they are Russian or Eastern European in origin, or are based upon servers in those countries, is not evidence of a link to traditional organised crime. Indeed, the new networked technologies used are relatively cheap, so there are comparatively few start-up costs and little upfront investment, plus they are online and do not need street protection - thus evading two well known hooks of traditional organised crime organisations.

Shadowcrew – Operation Firewall 2004/5 – the ShadowCrew were a gang dedicated to identity theft, bank account pillage, and the fencing stolen goods on the WWW. They did not meet.

Superzonda – spammers based in South America who specialize in creating and disseminating spam.

The Hangup Team – were a gang of Russians who develop malware for sale to hackers. They have links with the spamming industry which uses their botnets as spamming platforms.

The Rock Phish gang – were a notorious phishing gang that reinvented itself.

Drink or Die – a group that distributed Warez (pirated software). They claimed to be non profit, but were highly organized and security-conscious. They cracked the security in new software and then released it.

Carder Planet and Darkprofits – provided a www facility for selling credit card details

Rustock, Warezov, Blackcarder, Storm Worm Gang, Celebrity Spam Gang – each group controls botnets

The Russian Business Network – are responsible for drive-by downloads

Figure 1: Some of the cybercrime gangs known to have operated between 2000 and 2008

The key difference between cybercrime and traditional crime is its informational nature, networked structure and global reach (see BBC 2007; Goodin 2007a, b). True cybercrimes, those solely the product of the internet, but also those hybrid traditional crimes which have globalised opportunities are very different from traditional crimes that use the internet (Wall, 2007: 44-46). They are best understood as reflections of the new forms of social behaviours that are being fostered by networked technologies. So we find that cybercrime is increasingly taking on a 'Wikicrime' form of peer-production (for want of a better description – after Tapscott and Williams, 2007) as its organisation follows a Wiki model of organisation characterised by online collaborations rather than the 'command and control' Mafia model that is assumed by many. A useful example to hand of such a collaboration is the account in Wall 2007: 66-68) of an online group instructing a 'newbie' how to commit a hack. In this example, the group, because I resist using the term 'gang', in question is ordered only by a respect hierarchy and it is organised around the common interest in hacking chip security (for satellite receivers). In many ways cybercrimes, by their very informational, networked and global nature, go against the very grain of the traditional model of organised crime. Indeed, the following detailed example of scareware fraud and its organisation, upon which the remainder of this article is based, shows how the organisation of a true cybercrime closely imitates a flat e-commerce business model.

II. Scareware

'Scareware' is a type of malicious software that defrauds its victims by scaring them into paying for software that offers to fix their computer. Sometimes referred to 'rogueware', which is a less precise descriptor, scareware signifies an important trend in the evolution of cybercrime. Not only is it a good example of a 'true' cybercrime spawned purely by the internet (see further Wall, 2007, 2008), but possibly for the first time, it provides evidence of a complete crime being committed entirely by malicious software in large numbers. Software not only infects the victim's computer and conducts the scam, but it also takes the victim's money and deposits it into the offender's bank account. Other prevalent forms of 'true' cybercrime such as Phishing (ID Theft), by comparison, may also automated by software, but only to the extent that they scam, or socially engineer, personal financial information from victims and send it directly to the offenders. Offenders then need to employ a third party, typically a 'money mule', to use the stolen ID information to remove money from victim's accounts and pass it onto them.

A. How does scareware work?

Scareware is an aggressive fraud technique that uses routines set in malicious software (malware) to shock victims into paying for software that they do not need and which, in some cases, may actually cause further damage to their computers. User's computers are typically infected by emails that socially engineer them into opening infected attachments by clicking onto www sites, or by infecting frequently accessed and trusted www sites. The 'FakeAV153' Trojan, for example, found by Symantec to be the second most downloaded malware in 2009, displays false antivirus alerts and lowers security settings on compromised computers (Symantec, 2010). Once installed, the scareware remains dormant for a period of time so that the attack cannot be directly linked to the point of infection. The standard attack typically occurs when users will unexpectedly become inundated with messages that tell them their computer has been infected and that they have to immediately download, and pay for, software that will solve and prevent the problem, else (it is claimed) their system will be damaged permanently or even destroyed.

In its earliest forms, scareware savagely distressed its victims into complying. Typically the user's screen would freeze, as was the case with mid-2000s derivations of 'Nightmare' - the first scareware programme from 1991 (*India Times*, 2007). A skull would suddenly appear and emit a loud mocking shriek, alternatively the screen would appear to fragment and fall in pieces to the bottom of the monitor – and then the skill might appear. The action and message would panic victims into buying the software, but it would also leave them feeling cheated and humiliated. Scareware has subsequently evolved and more recent incarnations are becoming more professional in appearance. The most prevalent forms of scareware currently circulating, Antivirus 2009 and Antivirus XP, for example, have the general 'look and feel' of a major software brand, so much so that users find it hard to distinguish the scam 'pop up notices' from messages from their own operating system. See Figure 2. Some versions of scareware even maliciously suggest that it is being endorsed by the manufacturers (Leyden, 2009b).

The Scareware Scam – in five steps:

Step 1: Following download the 'fake' alert warning of a virus appears

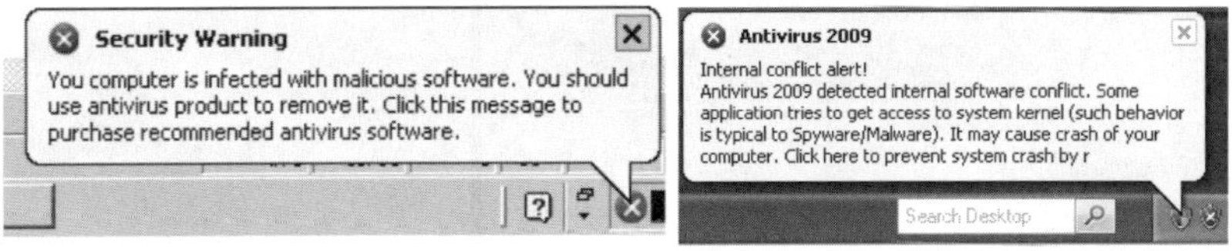

Step 2: Fake security warning mimicking the victim's operating system

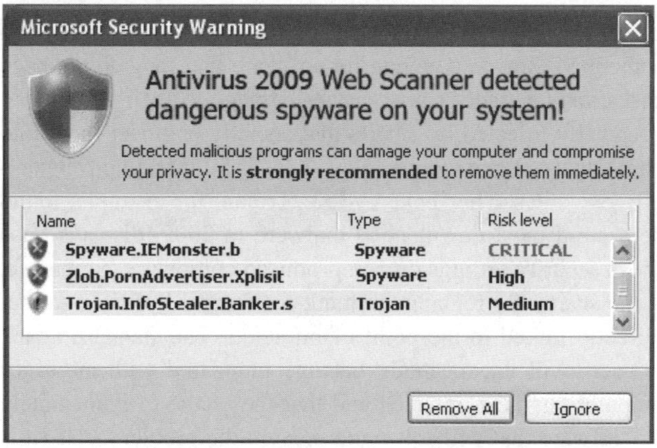

Step 3: Fake security center page mimicking the victim's operating system (top compared with the real security center down)

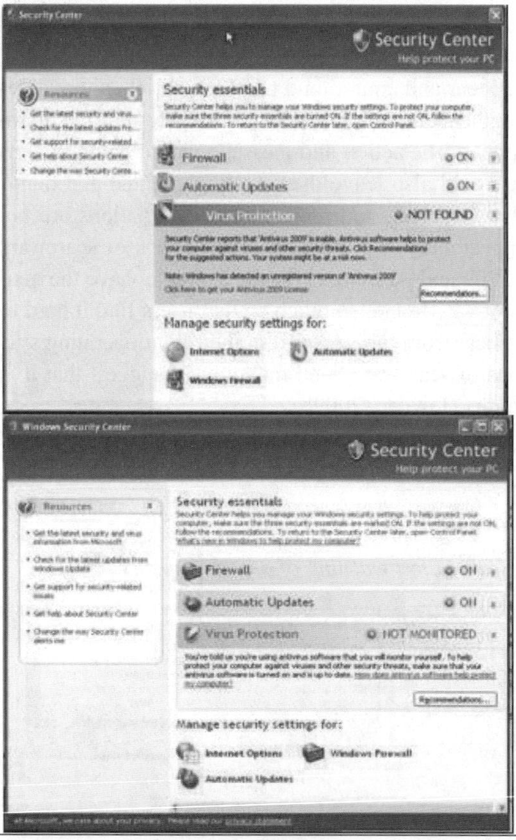

Step 4: The scan 'scam' in progress to raise anxiety and 'scare' victims

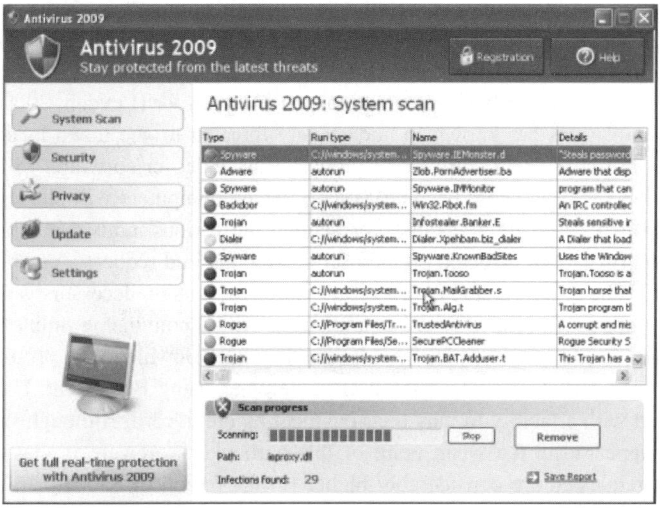

Step 5: The follow through 'scam' bombarding victims with messages until they purchase the anti-virus software (scareware)

Figure 2: Scareware scams in five steps (source for all images: Symantec, 2009b. Reproduction with the kind permission of Symantec).

More recent iterations of scareware in late 2009 and early 2010 scare victims into paying for a remedy, but by increasing victims' anxiety levels rather than by distressing them through shock. Some examples warn users that images of child pornography are located on their computer and state that they can only be removed with specialist removal software which has to be downloaded and paid for (Leyden, 2009a). Other (clever) adaptations are known to audaciously threaten to sue down-loaders who specifically use BitTorrent software to pirate music, video or software. In the scareware tradition (as it has now become), such infected computers will suddenly display a note from a company allegedly representing the various industries stating that pirated content has been detected on the user's computer and request a payment in compensation. Where this version of scareware varies from its predecessors is that a second pop-up notice subsequently presents the user with a convincing online invoice for a licence for the music, video or software they have downloaded - presumably based upon the actual downloads the user made when using BitTorrent. Users are also presented with a facility to may their payment by credit card. Although very professional in appearance, the weak point of this particular scareware is that the payments being requested are considerably higher (in the region of $400) than the $30 or being requested by the more conventional scareware and so jeopardise the scam by inciting victims to question or resist making the payment.

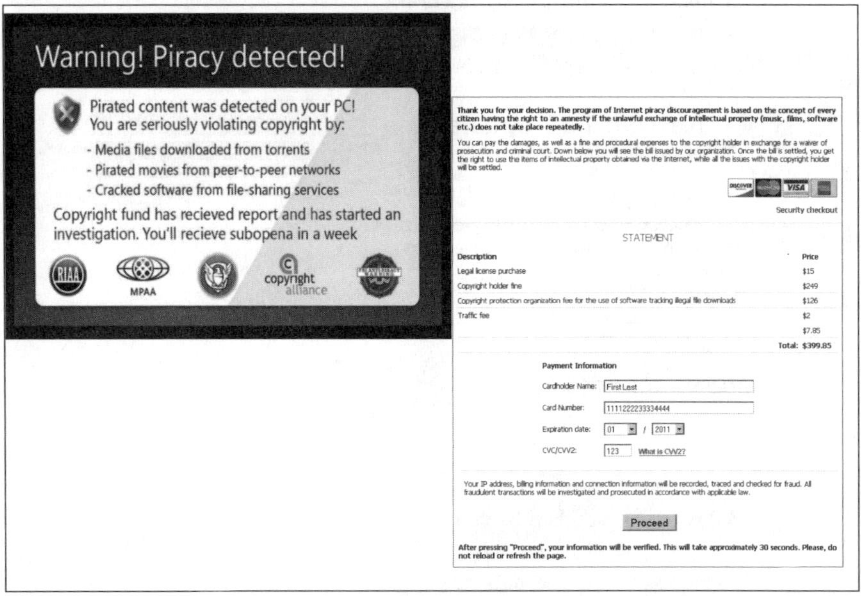

Figure 3: The Ransomware Scam (source: Kravets, 2010)

With most of the more recent examples of scareware, not only do the pop-notices convince victims that they have a genuine problem, but post-payment notices from the downloaded software indicate the removal of the malware and give the appearance of it actually having performed a therapeutic function. This helps reassure victims and leaves them feeling that they have been provided with the service that they paid for, not realising that they have been defrauded. In some cases, the scareware has been known to actually perform a basic and genuine function, such as clearing out unwanted or discarded files, which can frustrate attempts at a criminal prosecution.

B. How prevalent is the scareware threat?

The various annual threat reports from the cyber-security industry indicate a year-on-year increase in online threats. Symantec's computer security threat report for 2009, for example, shows that 1,656,277 cyber-threats were detected in 2008, which represented a 2.65 fold (1 million) increase when compared with 2007. In turn, the figures for 2007 represented a 4.4 fold increase on those for 2006 (Symantec, 2009a). Much of this increase can be explained by the rising threat of scareware which continued throughout 2009. In their October 2009 report on Rogueware, Symantec observed a dramatic increase in scareware threats during the first six months of the year in comparison to the last six months of 2008 and they identified 250 variants of scareware in circulation (Symantec, 2009b). The Anti-Phishing Working Group (APWG) similarly found that scareware threats had increased seven fold during the first half of 2009 from 22,218 in January to 152,197 in June (APWG, 2009: 1).

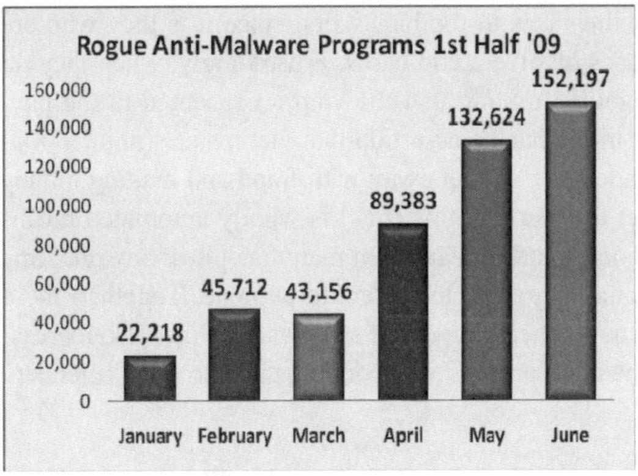

Figure 4: Rouge Anti-Malware Programs (Source: AWPG, 2009: 1)

The substantial increase in scareware threats was probably due to the increased use of search engine optimization (SEO) techniques used by Affiliates to assist them to distribute the scareware. In their scareware study, online security provider Finjan found that 1.8m unique users were redirected to rogue anti-virus site over a period of 16 consecutive days and that SEO techniques radically escalated the hit rate to between 7 and 12 per cent (Finjan, 2009: 4). Perhaps the most worrying findings are those from researchers from Google who, in analysing 13 months of reprocessed data from Google's malware detection infrastructure, found that fake anti-virus software (as it is also referred to) accounted for 15 percent of all types of malware identified by their search (Rajab et al., 2010; BBC, 2010). It is important to note here that not all of scareware threats will result in victimisation; however the indications are that many are doing so as the malware becomes more sophisticated.

C. How does scareware impact upon its victims?

When victimisation occurs, the average individual loss per victim to scareware is estimated to vary between US $10 and US $50 (Symantec, 2009b; Finjan, 2009); which is about the cost of a domestic security software package. Although these losses breach the fraud laws of most jurisdictions (e.g. s.7(1) UK Fraud Act 2006) they are a category of fraud that is becoming known as micro-frauds (Wall, 2010) and characterised by being individually small in impact, but significant only in their global aggregate. Importantly, they are deemed to be individually too small to be acted upon, often being written off by victims (both individual and corporate) or deemed not significant enough to devote policing resources to in the public interest (Wall, 2010). This characteristic causes particular reporting problems on the occasions when victims do feel victimised because not only may they be deterred from reporting them because of the complexities of the reporting process, but even if victims do report the fraud to police, then they are likely to feel dissatisfied. This is because police very often request that victims report their loss to the banks first since it is they who are regarded as the victims when losses involve credit cards. Frustratingly, when they do so the banks often refuse any liability arguing that the victim consented to the payment. Whilst there is some truth in the bank's assertion that victims are (unintentionally) complicit and willing, offenders are getting away with fraud and making money out of it (see later). Furthermore, the fact that this fraud is wholly automated means that the fraud is asymmetric and one fraudster can scam many people at any one time across jurisdictions, so the potential aggregate losses could be huge. Together, these factors combine to obscure the true financial impact of scareware, whilst also increasing the cash yield, speeding up the scam process and reducing the risk to the offender.

D. How are scareware scams organised?

The organisation of a typical scareware operation is effectively a 'criminal' reflection of the structure of 'Affiliate Marketing'; the popular internet based e-retailing practice (see Duffy, 2005). The 'Affiliate' model is not just found in cybercrimes that use computers, such as fraud, but also in the organisation of crimes against the machine (crimes against computer systems such as hacking etc.) and crimes in the machine (those crimes relating to the content of computers such as extreme pornography etc). A successful scareware project will require the establishment of a financial partnership between the 'Merchant' (or 'Kingpin') whose ideas initiate the project and who has access to the scareware to be used, an 'Affiliate' whose role it is to introduce the Merchant to the Consumer (e.g., by infecting victims' computers), and the Consumers ('victims') who are encouraged to part with their money. The Affiliates are employed on a pay-per-install basis and employ highly specialist computing techniques that use complex attack chains to infect mass numbers of victim's computers with the scareware. As found with mainstream Affiliate Marketing practices, a secondary tier of players, the 'brokers', has subsequently emerged to provide websites that bring together Kingpins and Affiliates and broker their relationship on a commission basis.

The relationship between the various actors involved is not the often assumed 'command and control' Mafia-type relationship, quite the opposite because the participants are distributed. In fact, it is highly likely that they never meet, so their relationships tend to be ephemeral and project based. Today, Kingpins seek to conduct their business as quietly as possible with a veneer of professionalism so as not to arouse their victims' suspicions. This is a marked change from the past when they used shock tactics to distress victims into paying up.

The relationship between the Kingpin and Affiliate is sometimes frustrated because the latter work to different criminal agenda and may not share the Kingpin's desire for stealth. This is because it is in the Affiliate's interest to maximise their own criminal opportunities by installing additional software, for example, malware linking them to botnets (robot networks of remotely administered computers) that will enable the Affiliates to independently access the victim's computer at a later date for their own criminal purposes. To protect themselves, Kingpins will not only pay affiliates a fee for the installation of the software on individual computers, usually in the region of $0.15 to $0.55 cents, sometimes more, but they may also compensate them for not injecting additional software into victim's computers that could unmask the scam. This compensation may be either a set fee or a proportion of the take from successful scams. Estimations of the sums of money yielded from scareware operations vary from report to report, but they are all large. Symantec have estimated that a full scareware operation can yield upwards of $850,000 (Symantec, 2009b) which represents approximately 30,000 scams of just under $30 each (my calculation). Such sums are entirely feasible since these scams take place on a global scale and that the scareware has the ability to route the profit straight into the offender's bank account. The actual recoverable gains do appear to be somewhat lower than the estimate, however, as is also found with recoveries from Phishing prosecutions, the recovered assets are still comparatively large. In June 2009, for example, two of a number of US defendants prosecuted by the Federal Trade Commission for a 'scareware' scam settled a $1.9m judgement against them for $116,697 worth of assets on the basis that they were unable to pay the full amount (FTC, 2009).

The implications of the scareware scam, its feasibility, its relative technical simplicity and the potential size of the yield are three fold. Firstly, it is highly likely that the overall number of offenders trying to emulate the financial success of the 'pioneer Kingpins' will quickly increase in number to diminish the individual yield and attractiveness of this sort of crime. Secondly, although the growth in size of the offender pool will increase the numbers of different scareware programmes circulating, many of these will be 're-skinned' (given a new appearance) or reverse engineered to create copies or variations of the originals. This means that the security industry, using its CAPTCHA software to discern between real and computer inputs and detect scareware and associated malware such as the spams which infect computers, can quickly close down the scammer's window of opportunity. It is also the case that press coverage of the threat reports which identified the initial scams informs computer users of the threat and makes them more suspicious of scareware, further reducing the likelihood of them falling for the scam. Thirdly, since there is now so much to gain financially, then the 'scareware-monger's' already accumulated criminal wealth and its associated power may be used to protect their own interests by 'policing' new offenders who enter the crime market. A trend found in 2009 with some of the more scurrilous scareware has been to encourage victims to buy the scareware solution bundled with branded proprietary security software at discounted rates to offset the victim's costs, but also to increase the victims trust because of the associated brand linkage. Of course the additional package rarely arrives and the purchaser then realises they have becomes a victim. Such activity threatens the business of both the stealthy Kingpin and also the legitimate security industry who will effectively act alongside (though not with) the former to protect their own interests by seeking to close down the offender.

It may even be the case that some of the original scareware Kingpins have already begun to abandon, re-skin or redeveloped their scareware in favour of more quasi-legitimate versions, but they will have successors. The advent of this type of wholly automated crime means that are entering the era of "the long tail" of crime (mimicking Chris Anderson's 2006 analysis of business in the information age). The future holds not just multiple victimisations from one scam, but multiple victimisations from multiple scams circulating at the same time. One criminal can now carry out many different automated crimes at the same time (Wall, 2007: 39). That is what is different about scareware.

E. What can we do about scareware?

As suggested earlier, the solution to scareware does not lie in creating new law because fraud and computer misuse are already illegal in most countries. Even the less invasive or detectable forms of scareware that do not breach criminal law are certainly covered by other law, and cases that emulate the look and feel of proprietary software can also breach intellectual property laws. Of all bodies of law, the strength of US law is probably the most important here since the majority of the scareware (53%) threats were found to come from computers based in the USA. The remainder were found in EU countries (20% +), with surprisingly small percentages in China (3%) or Russia (1%) (Symantec, 2009b) given the current media hype about computer misuse in those countries.

The main challenge to regulating scareware is that the offences arising from it are too small to act upon in the public interest and fall foul of the *de minimis* rule (Wall, 2007: 161). When combined with low levels of reporting by Individual victims, this characteristic limits potential criminal justice responses. Some law suits have been brought against Scareware operatives, such as the FTC case mentioned earlier, however, the case was settled prior to prosecution without any admission of guilt on the part of the defendants. Having said this, further legal action remains against others involved in the case and the defendants who settled were also prohibited by order from installing malicious programs on consumers' computers and employing 'scareware' tactics (FTC, 2009).

The most effective and quickest response to scareware (because the legal process can also be slow) is a combination of technological and educational solutions that narrow the criminal window of opportunity. Scareware can be quickly picked up by security software, and as with Phishing malware, computer users also quickly become aware of the potential risk it poses and cease to fall victim which makes them wary. Yet, scammers are becoming more adept at putting new spins on their trickery to undermine these counter-measures. They are quickly 're-skinning' their packages to give them a new look and feel and to make them much slicker (and as indicated earlier, more legitimate in terms of their claims) - which not only confuses users, but can also confuse the security technologies that use the checksum technique by changing the signature of the software's. But, since most victims of scareware tend to be those who possess insecure computers - which is how the malicious software usually gets through the firewall into the machine - then the best form of defence is to encourage users to keep their operating systems updated and also to install security software.

A major problem experienced to-date in policing the micro-frauds that result from the likes of scareware has been the lack of an effective, consistent and easy reporting system. This has long meant that crucial strategic intelligence which identifies 'the bigger picture' of impact at a nation level has been lost, as has the important tactical criminal intelligence relating to the offenders, which hampers the police ability to investigate. Hopefully, new arrangements under the UK's *Cyber Security Policy* (Cabinet Office, 2009), complemented by the new *UK Cyber Crime Strategy* (Home Office, 2010) will combine with the *National Fraud Strategy* (NFA, 2009) and *E-crime Policing Strategy* (ACPO, 2009) to help to address the problem of scareware (NFA, 2009). As part of that policy, the Action Fraud reporting centre (referred to in earlier documentation as the National Fraud Reporting Centre and now supported by the National Fraud Authority), has from late 2009 received reports of fraud, including scareware related fraud. These and reports of other types of fraud and related cybercrime are then passed on to the National Fraud Information Bureau (NFIB) which analyses and builds up a national picture of online fraud. Located within the City of London Police, the NFIB also decides how the reported frauds are to be acted upon through its national tasking system (Cabinet Office, 2009). The NFIB works alongside the National Police Central e-Crime Unit (PCeU) which is based in the Metropolitan Police and set up as part of the ACPO National e-Crime Strategy (ACPO, 2009). The PCeU also operates in close collaboration with the Metropolitan Police's own Dedicated Cheque and Plastic Card Unit (DCPCU) which focuses upon the physical corruption of technological devices used in the banking system.

When frauds are found to have caused significant losses, or are clearly the product of organised crime, then the Serious Fraud Office or the e-crime unit of the Serious Organised Crime Agency (SOCA) may become involved. Whilst the many different types of policing organisations working in the field create an adverse potential for 'turf wars', they and their 'nested' parent strategies nevertheless represent a positive step towards providing a system of combating cybercrime related fraud at a national level - only time will tell whether or not these arrangements will be effective.

III. Conclusion

The Scareware story and those of other true cybercrimes seem a million miles away from the vision of traditional organised crime invoked in Mario Puza's various Mafia novels, and indeed they are. At first sight many involved in law enforcement can be forgiven for either not seeing what the fuss is about, or simply seeing cybercrime as a technical problem. This is because their view of the world is largely based upon Peelian (after Robert Peel, the founder of modern policing) principles of policing in order to keep the dangerous classes off the streets, to maintain order and also enforce law. But, it is argued here that true cybercrimes are of crucial significance because the malicious software's high level of automation, its ability to victimise asymmetrically and the capacity to manage fraudulently obtained gains represents a step change in online criminal practices. In this sense cybercrime has come of age and now poses a significant threat.

In understanding that threat it is important to acknowledge the different ways that cybercrimes are organised. The very nature of (true) cybercrimes being informational, global and networked (and increasingly automated) has encouraged different, flatter, forms of organisation than the hierarchies of control found in more traditional forms of offending. The technologies allow far fewer people to control the whole criminal process, even fewer when the crime is automated as with scareware, and networking process tends to undermine attempts to effect control Wall, 2007: 39). However, whilst scareware, phishing and other forms of cybercrime do not display the classic signs of organised crime, they do display distinctively different organisational traits, not least their ephemeral nature, their stealth and a marked similarity to an unethical e-commerce business model rather than the Mafia. What this tells us is that the organisation of crime online follows a different logic to both organised crime and also the organisation of crime offline. This is an observation that has implications both for law enforcement as well as prevention, because it is a logic that lends itself to a relativist rather than absolutist conceptualisation of cybercrime that is so often encountered. In other words, cybercrime by its very nature cannot be eradicated, it can only regulated and managed to minimise its impacts, this means that counter-cybercrime strategies, including prevention, therefore needs to focus upon much more upon the regulation and management of cybercrime, including, but not exclusively, using disruptive technologies, in order to minimise its impact.

NOTE: This project began during a fellowship kindly awarded by CEPS, the Australian Research Council's Centre for Excellence in Policing and Security at the ANU, Canberra and Griffith's University, Brisbane, Australia, it was subsequently developed through participation with the Cybercrime Research Group at the Max Planck Institute (*Phillip Brunst*, *Marcello Bellini*, *Jochen Jähnke* and *Jan Spoenle*). I would like to thank both research groups.

REFERENCES

- ACPO (2009) *ACPO e-Crime Strategy*, Association of Chief Police Officers, http://www.acpo.police.uk/asp/policies/data/Ecrime%20Strategy%20Website%20Version.pdf
- ANDERSON, C. (2006) *The Long Tail: Why the Future of Business is Selling Less of More*, New York: Hyperion.
- APWG (2009) *Phishing Activity Trends Report, 1st Half 2009*, Anti-Phishing Working Group, http://www.antiphishing.org/reports/apwg_report_h1_2009.pdf
- BBC (2007) 'Arrests made in botnet crackdown', *BBC News Online*, 30 November, [Online] Available at: http://news.bbc.co.uk/1/hi/technology/7120251.stm (30 January 2008).
- BBC (2010) 'BBC Google warning on fake anti-virus software', *BBC News Online*, 28 April, http://news.bbc.co.uk/1/hi/technology/10088949.stm
- BRENNER, S. (2002) 'Organized cybercrime? How cyberspace may affect the structure of criminal relationships', *North Carolina Journal of Law & Technology*, vol. 4, no. 1, pp. 1–41.
- CABINET OFFICE (2009) *Cyber Security Strategy of the United Kingdom: safety, security and resilience in cyber space*, http://www.cabinetoffice.gov.uk/media/216620/css0906.pdf
- C'T (2004) 'Uncovered: trojans as spam robots', *C'T Magazine*, 23 February, [Online] Available at: www.heise.de/english/newsticker/news/44879 (30 January 2008).
- DUFFY, D. (2005) 'Affiliate marketing and its impact on e-commerce', *Journal of Consumer Marketing*, 22(3): 161 – 163.
- FINJAN (2009) 'Finjan Discovers a Network of 1.9 Million Malware-Infected Computers Controlled by Cybercriminals - Corporate and Government Computers Are Included', *Finjan Press Release*, 22 April, http://www.finjan.com/Pressrelease.aspx?id=2238&PressLan=2139&lan=3
- FTC (2009) 'FTC Settles with Two Defendants in Bogus Computer Scan Case', *Federal Trade Commission press release*, 25 June, http://www.ftc.gov/opa/2009/06/winsoftware.shtm
- GOODIN, D. (2007a) 'Botmaster owns up to 250,000 zombie PCs: He's a security consultant. Jail beckons', *The Register*, 9 November, [Online] Available at: http://www.theregister.co.uk/2007/11/09/botmaster_to_plea_guilty/ (30 January 2008).
- GOODIN, D. (2007b) 'FBI crackdown on botnets gets results, but damage continues: 2 million zombies and counting', *The Register*, 29 November, [Online] Available at: http://www.theregister.co.uk/2007/11/29/fbi_botnet_progress_ report/ (30 January 2008).

- HOME OFFICE (2010) *Cyber Crime Strategy*, Cm 7842, London: Office of Public Sector Information, March, http://www.official-documents.gov.uk/document/cm78/7842/7842.pdf
- INDIA TIMES (2007) 'Scareware: Playing on your fears!', *India Times*, 21 February, http://infotech.indiatimes.com/articleshow/1653102.cms
- KRAVETS, D. (2010) 'Malware Threatens to Sue BitTorrent Downloaders', *Wired Threat Level blog*, 12 April, http://www.wired.com/threatlevel/2010/04/ransomware/
- LEYDEN, J. (2009a) 'Scareware tool dumps smut on Windows PCs: Rogue clean-up tool poses child abuse frame risk, *The Register*, 19 November, http://www.theregister.co.uk/2009/11/19/smut_scareware/
- LEYDEN, J. (2009b) 'Scareware slingers flaunt fake MS endorsement', *The Register*, 10 December, http://www.theregister.co.uk/2009/12/10/scareware_fake_ms_endorsement/
- NFA (2009) *The National Fraud Strategy*: A new approach to combating fraud, National Fraud authority/ Attorney General's Office, http://www.attorneygeneral.gov.uk/NewsCentre/News/Documents/NFSA_STRATEGY_AW_Web%5B1%5D.pdf
- NISCC (2005) 'Targeted trojan email attacks', *NISCC Briefing* 08/2005, 16 June, [Online] Available at: http://www.cpni.gov.uk/Docs/ttea.pdf (30 January 2008).
- RAJAB, M., BALLARD, L, MAVROMMATIS, P., PROVOS, N. and ZHAO, X. (2010) *The Nocebo Effect on theWeb: An Analysis of Fake Anti-Virus Distribution*, Santa Clara: Google Inc., http://krebsonsecurity.com/wp-content/uploads/2010/04/leet10.pdf
- RODGERS, L. (2007) 'Smashing the criminals' e-bazaar', *BBC News Online*, 20 December, [Online] Available at: http://news.bbc.co.uk/1/hi/uk/7084592.stm (30 January 2008).
- SYMANTEC (2009a) *Internet Security* Threat Report *Volume XIV: April,* 2009, http://www.symantec.com/business/theme.jsp?themeid=threatreport
- SYMANTEC (2009b) *Symantec Report on Rogue Security Software July 2008 - June 2009*, October, http://eval.symantec.com/mktginfo/enterprise/white_papers/b-symc_report_on_rogue_security_software_WP_20016952.en-us.pdf
- SYMANTEC (2010) *Symantec Global Internet Security Threat Report Trends for 2009*, Volume XV, April. http://eval.symantec.com/mktginfo/enterprise/white_papers/b-whitepaper_internet_security_threat_report_xv_04-2010.en-us.pdf
- TAPSCOTT, D. and Williams, A. (2007) *Wikinomics: How mass collaboration changes everything*, London: Atlantic Books.
- WALL, D.S. (2007) *Cybercrime: The transformation of crime in the information age*, Cambridge: Polity
- WALL, D.S. (2008) 'Old tricks, new dogs - How to regulate cybercrimes', *Jane's Intelligence Review*, vol. 20, no. 10, pp: 45-47.
- WALL, D.S. (2010) 'Micro-frauds: Virtual Robberies, Stings and Scams in the Information Age', in T. Holt, T., and B. Schell (eds) *Corporate Hacking and Technology-Driven Crime: Social Dynamics and Implications*, Hershey, PA (USA): IGI Global.
- WALL, D.S. (2010) 'Taking fright - The growing threat of scareware', *Jane's Intelligence Review*, vol. 22, no. 5, pp. 40-43
- WARREN, P. (2005) 'UK trojan siege has been running over a year', *The Register*, 17 June, [Online] Available at: www.theregister.co.uk/2005/06/17/niscc_ warning/ (30 January 2008).

Jan Spoenle

Underground Economy

An overview on professional cybercrime business and the legal challenges that come along with it

This article discusses the current state of the cybercrime business. It takes into account the tools and business structures discovered and reported by IT security companies and information technology researchers as well as information from expert interviews conducted with law enforcement officials in Germany and Switzerland. Furthermore, the article deals with the ramifications of a growing sophistication in cybercrime business organization for law enforcement in practice and the legal battle against cybercrime in general with respect to the German criminal code and criminal procedure code.

In the years since 2005, the existence of some kind of "underground economy" devoted to cybercrime has become widely known in a sense of notoriety. What public knowledge, formed by press reports, dismissed only a few years ago as the pranks of adolescent "computer freaks" seems to have changed into a highly professional and organized underground industry that is networked around the globe and operates for the most part clandestinely. While the exact extent of the cybercrime business remains unclear due to a lack of reliable numbers – press reports about billions of dollars earned in cybercrime are probably largely exaggerated and based on assumptions (*Poulsen*, 2007), and alarming IT security reports might as well be fueled by business motives – the available information gives enough reasons to worry about future development: for instance, there is no reason to doubt the modi operandi described by the IT security community, especially as police investigators begin to publicly depict the same methods and tools (*Manske*, 2007). And while "Phishing" itself might not be as rewarding as many first thought (*Herley, Florêncio*, 2008), law enforcement authorities should also focus on those who provide the necessary tools and services behind the scenes.

I. The Cybercrime Business Ecosystem

Due to its swift and intangible nature, describing the cybercrime business ecosystem has always been a challenging task. *Bolduan* (2008) however managed not only to give a comprehensive overview, but also delivered a graphic chart showing a cycle on which the first part of this article and the original presentation is based. Though labeled in German, the graphic chart should be quite easy to understand as it uses typical cybercrime terms in English. The following sections A – D describe what can be seen in the graphic chart starting in the upper left quarter and moving counterclockwise.

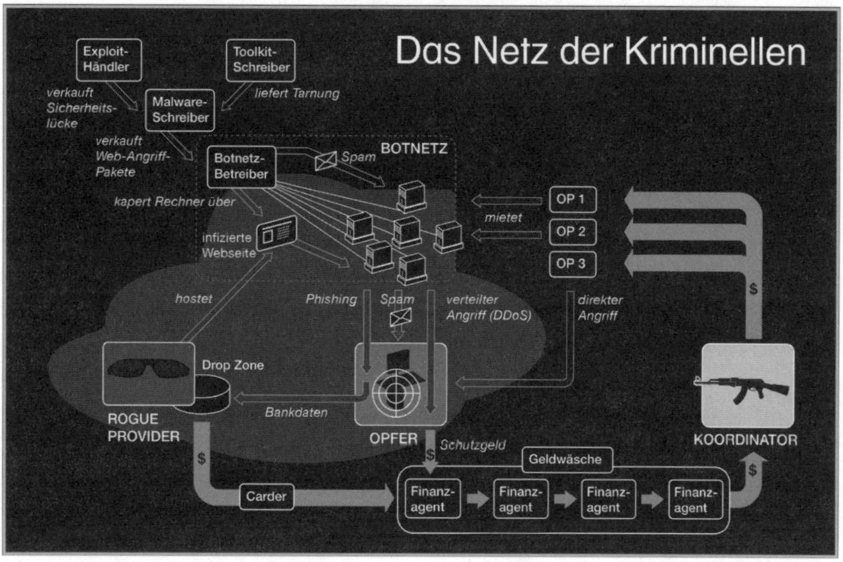

Figure courtesy of Technology Review Germany, Heise Zeitschriften Verlag, Hannover

A. Malware & Exploits for Sale

Hacking, or gaining control over other machines within a network, is still the starting point for most serious cybercrimes. But where it used to be manual work in the 1990s, demanding substantial skills and thus being suitable for romanticizing in the press and fiction, it's nowadays a mere question of automation. Of course, the tools for automating the hacking part of the business are on sale (*Krebs*, 2007): the scope of the market encompasses web-based standard attack kits as well as tailor-made trojan horse software, offered with 24/7 support via IRC channels, Skype or VoIP calls if desired (*Bachfeld*, 2008; *Fossi et. al.*, 2008: 28 ff.). Some IT professionals working in the underground economy specialize in reviewing code, looking for exploits, while others offer expertise in writing malware using the newly discovered loopholes (*Bolduan*, 2008: 28 f.; *MELANI*, 2008: 35 ff.). Bringing together experts from different areas generates benefits just as it does for the world of legal business.

Just as hacking changed from a manual to an automated business, infection vectors for malware have also evolved, becoming more professional and less detectable. Due to public attention and education through the media, the success of delivering malware within e-mail attachments diminished recently; instead, malware is distributed through infected P2P downloads and malicious or – even more dangerous – hacked legitimate websites, putting so-called drive-by-downloads into operation (*BSI*, 2009: 21; *Bolduan*, 2008: 28). The main objective achieved by malware is still to gather all kinds of data: credit card numbers, bank account details, software license keys and other serial numbers. But recently, additional business models like selling scareware or blackmailing through ransomware came into fashion: while scareware pretends to be legitimate anti-virus software, telling victims that their machine can only be cleaned up if they pay a certain amount to license the rogue and mostly useless product, ransomware encrypts certain files, all files of a certain kind (e.g. MS Word documents) or whole partitions – of course, the victims need to pay before they can decrypt and access their precious data again. Furthermore, specialized malware like banking trojans is deployed in order to circumvent security measures by hooking itself up with SSL-secured communications between bank and user machines as a "man-in-the-middle" (*Ståhlberg*, 2007).

B. Botnet Infrastructure

The ultimate goal of infecting victims' machines, however, is building up a botnet infrastructure, which is considered *the* most dangerous and malicious cybercrime threat right now – for instance, the European Network and Information Security Agency (ENISA) called botnets "a steadily increasing problem threatening governments, industries, companies and individual users with devastating consequences" two years ago (*Barroso*, 2007: 1). In the meantime, of course, the technology and capabilities of botnet infrastructure have advanced: what used to be relatively small amounts of computers remotely controlled by a single and thus easy to snipe IRC command-&-control server (*Holz et. al.*, 2007: 1) has grown into a phenomenon involving huge, scalable networks of home and/or business PCs infected with malware – so-called bot clients, which listen for orders given by the bot herder in charge through RSS feeds, communicating via P2P and domain-flux technology (*Fossi et. al.*, 2008: 29; *Stone-Gross et. al.*, 2009: 3) and – recently – even using Twitter (*Singel*, 2009) to deliver coordinating measures. Botnets offer a vast bandwidth perfomance which, for example, can be used to blackmail Internet businesses that rely on connectivity: if the victim is unwilling to pay, its website might be unavailable for days due to distributed denial of service attacks. Furthermore, the bot client running on an infected PC can – and in most cases will – also be used to distribute keyloggers and other malware that facilitates identity theft and identity fraud by collecting personal data (see above). Some bot herders even set up affiliate networks and pay their partners for additional infections, as shown in the case of the "Golden Cash platform" (*Finjan*, 2009).

Primarily, however, botnets are used as an infrastructure that can be rented out to third parties – rental price lists for bot clients show that single bots are quite cheap, while it's more expensive to have the bot herder carry out a certain attack (*Namestnikov*, 2009). Since bot herders need to care for their botnet – keeping it out of the danger to be shut down, kicking out defunct bots and updating working bots to stay ahead of the anti-virus software products – they probably don't have the time to exploit its capabilities themselves. The services they offer include the dissemination of millions of spam e-mails without the risk of being traced back to the origin of the junk mail as well as automated phishing schemes targeting bank customers worldwide, though there is usually some specialization on certain countries and banks. Another reason for potential customers to rent botnet infrastructure is using the bots as proxy machines: connecting over a local bot machine or "zombie PC" offers the advantage of using a local IP address for circumvention of regional IP fraud detection systems – for instance, a U.S. bank might get suspicious if the perpetrator logs into an account with an IP address from Ukraine – and a relatively good chance of anonymity, since the only trace leads to some unsuspecting home PC user that didn't even know his or her machine were part of a criminal network.

The data collected by bot clients and their specialized malware siblings will usually be encrypted and stored in so-called drop zones (*Bolduan*, 2008: 31 f.) – either a hacked web server or online storage intentionally set up only to serve as dead mail drop. From there, it can be picked up by a purchaser and traded on IRC channels and web forums devoted to the underground economy, like the recently shut down 'DarkMarket' (*Poulsen*, 2008). More likely, however, the loot will be passed on to the next part of the cybercrime business ecosystem – the people who turn data into cash.

C. Transforming Data into Money

The process of cashing in on stolen data – no matter what kind of data – is the most challenging part of the cybercrime business (*Thomas*, *Martin*, 2006: 11), and probably still the part which is least understood by researchers as well as law enforcement officials. While it's quite easy to imagine how login credentials for virtual payment services like paypal.com or webmoney.ru can be monetized, it's not that obvious for gaming accounts like the wildly popular World of Warcraft. Also, transferring virtual money out of hacked payment accounts and into the perpetrator's bank account would boost chances to get caught significantly. Therefore, there have to be more clandestine ways to transform data into money.

First, there is the carding scene helping to monetize on credit card numbers and the magnetic stripe information gathered by the skimming community from ATMs (for a comprehensive introduction to the world of carding see *Zetter*, 2007). Carders create fake credit cards with stolen data, so-called "white plastic", and employ low-level criminals – so-called "money mules" – to take the cards to ATMs and withdraw cash. Another option for stolen credit card numbers is to use them as payment method on Amazon.com and similar web shops; then, however, real world drop locations are needed to pick up the ordered goods – which are just another service on offer within the cybercrime business (*Fossi et. al.*, 2008: 18). The phishing branch of the underground economy has different needs: because phishing is done by moving money directly out of the victims' bank accounts and thus traceable, the perpetrators need the help of financial agents who process the stolen money through their own private bank account, withdraw the received sum and – after taking out their interest – send it to their masters using a cash transfer service like Western Union. Financial agents are primarily unemployed people or otherwise susceptible to get-rich-quick schemes advertised through spam e-mails (*Bolduan*, 2008: 31). Local money mules pick up the transferred cash abroad, only having to know about a certain transfer code number, or sometimes using a forged passport (*Debrebant*, 2008).

A third option to turn data into cash and vice versa without leaving traces is offered by debit card services. A debit card vendor will rely on a network of so-called "exchangers", who accept payments in different currencies and through various channels – including virtual payment services – in order to charge the customer's debit card. The latter might then be used to withdraw money in cash or to transfer any balance left on the card back to a virtual payment service; the only requirement in order to do so is using the service of another exchanger, who in turn bills some kind of interest for his help. Exchangers do not keep records of the identity of their customers, and besides the use case described above, there are perfectly legal needs for their business model, e.g. transferring precious assets from one virtual payment service to another, between different gaming accounts or withdrawing money from a virtual payment service after an online deal or eBay sale could not be concluded.

D. Masterminds and Cybercrime Havens

All of the above, however, can't be done without the proper infrastructure and services behind the scenes: for instance, if criminals would start a phishing scam using illegitimate websites hosted by a renowned big player in the Internet economy, the latter would be interested in getting rid of their criminal customers as soon as possible and shutting the sites down on notice from law enforcement authorities. Also, the availability of "crimeware as a service" – according to the term "software as a service", short SaaS, this business model refers to a completely hosted solution for distributing malware, including the automated retrieval and quality assessment of stolen data within dropzone locations without any installation and configuration hassles for the criminal customer (*Stone-Gross et. al.*, 2009: 8; *Faber*, 2008: 94 f.) – points towards a well-organized world of hosters and Internet service providers willing or solely devoted to serving criminal needs: the so-called "rogue providers".

One of the most notorious services offered by rogue providers is "bulletproof hosting", i.e. shielding customers from complaints about domain abuse and not being overly helpful towards law enforcement authorities' attempts to disconnect the site in question (*Bolduan*, 2008: 32; *Faber*, 2008: 93). Bulletproof hosting is everything but cheap, and often the fee depends on the amount of incoming abuse complaints, thus letting the rogue provider profit from the customer's success. Other services include the possibility to rapidly change and adapt DNS records for fast-flux-networks (*Faber*, 2008: 96). In order to fulfill the needs of their customers, it's important for rogue providers to be well connected, ensuring high bandwidth and many options for IP routes – a skill mastered perfectly by the Russian Business Network (RBN), one of the early big players in the underground economy, by accumulating satellite Internet providers connected to many autonomous systems (*Bizeul*, 2008: 11 ff.).

While there are speculations about rogue providers being run by traditional organized crime groups to a certain extent as an auxiliary business to drug and human trafficking, so far no clear evidence of this has been found. Similarly, despite speculations about Eastern Europe and Russia being some kind of safe haven for cybercrime activities, IT security researchers and law enforcement officials have never confirmed specific "cybercrime states"; on the contrary, the case studies concerning the California based rogue providers McColo and Atrivo (*Armin*, 2008) show that the underground economy is not primarily looking for an insufficient legal situation or deficient law enforcement, but for connectivity and bandwidth in abundance.

II. Challenges for Law Enforcement

A lack of legal instruments and adequate action by law enforcement, however, would surely be greatly appreciated on the side of cybercrime business. Also, aside from wild guesswork on billions earned in cybercrime as mentioned above but based on reports from institutions like the U.S. Internet Crime Complaint Center (2005 – 2009), it seems safe to assume that the profits generated by the underground economy increase steadily – and as more and more parts of our analog lives go digital, this trend is likely to continue. Therefore, conclusions drawn from watching the development of modi operandi should be picked up by legislators and practicioners in order to adjust the arsenal of legal instruments as well as the deployment and proper training of technically savvy personnel to the conditions of the digital world. The following subsections look into the current trends in cybercrime with respect to future focal points of criminal activity and remaining drawbacks on the national – German – and international level.

A. Current Trends: What to Expect

Since banks, virtual payment services and other main targets of cybercriminal activities start to shift their attention towards security measures, thus making it harder for perpetrators to successfully defraud their customers, the attention of the cybercrime business seems to have also shifted at least in parts: concurrent reports of IT security and anti-virus companies point out that the online gaming sector shows significant growth in malicious activities (*Hayashi*, 2009; *Urbanski*, 2009). While more and more malware code newly found in the wild turns out to be gaming trojans or keyloggers trying to grab users' credentials for popular online games like World of Warcraft, the availability of stolen or compromised gaming accounts consequently increased faster than that of other identity theft related account data. The reason for this, as usual, is pecuniary interest: within gaming platforms, certain virtual markets have emerged where virtual goods are traded in-game – such as armament, apparel or special skills for the players' avatar. In order to cash in on the passion of players, gaming providers created virtual payment systems and virtual currencies within games; real money can be used to fill up the balance, and virtual gains and assets within the game can be reconverted to real money. This, of course, is a perfect ecosystem for money laundering; moving incriminated assets and hiding their true source has never been easier.

Another trend, though more of technological nature, that is going to have an impact on the way cybercrime can and should be fought emerges in cloud computing.[1] The concept of cloud computing relies on the fact that location does not matter to data and/or users under the conditions of broadband Internet connections. Therefore, the hosting of data, of single services or whole application suites is offered as a service itself that is accessible over a broadband connection; the actual computing and storage takes place in "the cloud", i.e. the cloud computing providers' networks (*Wikipedia*, Cloud Computing, 2009). While there is a lot of benefit in this rapidly developing business model for customers with honest and dishonest intentions alike, especially the latter might profit from a situation of uncertainty created by cloud computing for law enforcement: when some fuzzy logic algorithm decides where to store data at what time and how to move it around in order to save money, the location of a certain piece of information might be unpredictable even for the cloud computing provider at a given moment. But territory is still crucial in terms of jurisdiction.

B. Legal Drawbacks in Germany

However, territorial trouble does not only apply to issues on the international level: even within a single jurisdiction, regional fragmentation of competencies can lead to legal drawbacks with respect to high volume crimes. Phishing, for example, is known to be some kind of bulk business – the perpetrators send out thousands of bait spam messages and wait for victims to deliver their credentials unsuspectingly, or they try to infect victims at random through drive-by-downloads, using malware to gain access to the victims' bank accounts. In both instances, these crimes happen

---

1 See "Consequences of Cloud Computing" by *Schneider* on pp. 83 et seq. for further details on this matter.

in waves and usually affect people anywhere in the target region – which is where the customers of the target bank(s) live. When the victims report these crimes, each prosecutor's office involved might probably see two, three or even five of these reports; as there is no special competency for cybercrime in most areas of Germany, even different prosecutors might be working the different cases coming up in one single office. This way it remains unkown to each of the territorial neighbouring prosecutors' offices involved that the cases are not single crimes involving computer fraud, but identical acts of computer fraud most likely committed by an individual group of fraudsters.

But, if by any chance or future administrative measure – a greater concentration of competency for cybercrime, for example – the similarities would be recognized, this would change the way the cases could be investigated by law enforcement to a great extent: computer fraud, as well as fraud itself, are crimes mentioned in section 100a paragraph II of the German code of criminal procedure (Strafprozessordnung, abbrev. StPO), which deals with the authorization of wiretapping as an investigative measure. According to the provisions of this section, if the cases altogether sum up to a reasonable suspicion of computer fraud committed either on a repetitive basis to contribute to a living or by a gang acting on a regular basis, the authorization to wiretap the suspects might be obtained. Also, the list in section 100a paragraph II StPO is not only applicable to wiretapping, but vitally important for other – mostly covert – investigative measures that might be available and helpful if connections between identical phishing cases become visible to the prosecutors.

The very same legal architecture prevents the use of such investigative measures in cases where only prerequisites to most cybercrimes are discovered or traceable so far: the provisions in German substantive criminal code regarding illegal access to computer systems, illegal interception of data traffic and illegal alteration, suppression or deletion of data (sections 202a, 202b and 303a of the Strafgesetzbuch, abbrev. StGB) are neither included in section 100a paragraph II StPO, nor do they provide for aggravating circumstances if committed on a repetitive basis or by a gang. However, section 303b StGB – regarding computer sabotage by severely disrupting the operation of a computer system – provides for such aggravating circumstances in paragraph IV. But this only applies to disrupting the operation of a computer system used by a company or an authority, and section 303b StGB is not listed in section 100a paragraph II StPO as well; therefore, sophisticated and covert investigative measures are not available in cases of hacking and man-in-the-middle attacks as long as the perpetrators do not use the access or information gained to defraud the victim.

Another drawback is the lack of some investigatory tools that become more and more important as digital communications gain popularity. For instance, it is still unclear if wiretapping warrants can be issued legally for surveillance of Skype Internet telephony: as the Skype protocol provides for a strong user-to-user encryption, the only way to wiretap is to grab the audio signal before it is processed by the

Skype software, which can only be done by compromising the suspect's machine. Since the federal state of North-Rhine-Westphalia tried to equip its intelligence service with the option to use a covert software – having become infamous later on as the "federal trojan" which is now an option for the federal police in combating terrorism – to monitor suspects' file systems and behaviour, a fierce discussion on investigatory measures and the right to privacy has begun in Germany that is far from over; while the federal constitutional court did not hesitate to rescind the North-Rhine-Westphalian law, it also left options to design such a measure in line with constitutional requirements (*Bundesverfassungsgericht*, 2008). As of now, however, the use of CIPAV-like measures (*Wikipedia*, Computer and Internet Protocol Address Verifier, 2009) is not permitted for law enforcement authorities.

Furthermore, the principle of mandatory prosecution provided for in section 152 paragraph II StPO poses practical problems for law enforcement authorities in cybercrime scenarios. Also called the principle of legality, the provision obliges law enforcement officials to prosecute any crime they come across. In practice, this obligation might obstruct helpful investigations of a more general nature in order to highlight modi operandi and other context information probably useful in future cases: by filing a single case for each and every piece of criminal content and other data pointing towards crimes found on a hacked server – such as child pornography, botnet control components, thousands of sets of stolen personal information data etc. – the bureaucratic effort exceeds the outcome of these John Doe cases by far and not only binds resources, but would also cause a sharp rise of unsolved cybercrime cases, which will be statistically and politically undesirable. Therefore, law enforcement authorities tend to shy away from examining sample data offered by white hat hackers and other members of the IT security community.

C. International and Interdisciplinary Cooperation

A totally different principle is at the forefront of practical problems for investigations in international contexts: the principle of territoriality. It's a basic principle of public international law denying state A's law enforcement authorities the right to act within state B – and vice versa – and can be amended by treaties for exceptions such as cross-border pursuits (*Meyer-Goßner*, 2008: 54). In cybercrime scenarios, it prevents law enforcement authorities from investigating data stored on servers abroad. Of course, neither the technical architecture of digital networks nor the criminals making use of them care much for traditional borders and territory; in fact, the criminals might even be encouraged to store data in countries from which they have to fear prosecution the least – or which hesitate to cooperate with prosecuting states. In addition, the legal instruments developed to ensure cooperation between states in criminal procedure matters reflects a heritage of diplomacy and could use serious improvements especially concerning speed: where data is moved, altered and deleted in milliseconds, the judicial assistance system works with letters and printed files sent from the requesting prosecutor over his or her supervising authority through the diplomatic channels, which might only take a few days, but sometimes can take up to several years; sometimes there is no answer at all. In the meantime, however, crucial evidence might be lost or tampered with by foreign investigators with less experience or training. One possible solution might be to take a different approach to the way data is currently treated in procedural regulations: instead of location as point of reference for the assessment of procedural actions such as search and seizure, future regulations and/or international agreements might favor the suspect's power of disposal with respect to an account, folders or single files on a server – no matter where that server is actually located. This would also avoid the problem of picking locations and thus jurisdictions at random by using cloud computing technology (see above). However, this approach needs further research, as there seem to be serious collateral issues with search and seizure of data across borders especially between states and regimes with tense relations. For the time being, article 32 paragraph b of the Council of Europe's Convention on Cybercrime (CoE CCC, available online at http://conventions.coe.int/Treaty/EN/Treaties/Html/185.htm) shows that a power-of-disposal approach is possible and useful to some extent; also, articles 29 and 30 CoE CCC should be very helpful in speeding up international cooperation. Unfortunately, not all signature states have also ratified the convention yet, while important Council of Europe members like Russia and Turkey haven't even signed the convention.

But there's more to the term cooperation in fighting cybercrime than inter-state judicial assistance: another level of cooperation should certainly be a more constructive collaboration between law enforcement authorities and the private sector. It is often argued that there seems to be some kind of coexistance instead of cooperation with respect to the IT community on the one hand and the law enforcement community on the other (*Ries*, 2009). While the former concentrate on defending their systems, products and services, thus only leaving the perpetrators with more "homework" to be done for their next attempt, the latter have to identify and prosecute the responsible individuals, seeking a more or less durable solution – but are deprived from the chance to watch, study and learn from modi operandi. It's quite obvious that both communities would profit from a combined approach; effective general deterrence – which criminal law is aspiring to by prosecuting and sentencing offenders – might help to decrease the attack volume fought by IT security professionals. The South Korean CERT's model of fighting off attacks as an intermediary between law enforcement and the private sector could serve as an example: with amplified competencies, the South Korean CERT is to be informed by the private sector about malicious traffic on a regular short-term basis and will then take appropiate measures, but also collect data that can be used for a subsequent investigation by the public sector (*Ries*, 2009). Regardless of future provisions in such an approach or best practice guidelines, however, international solutions should be preferred – at least on the intermediary level, appropiate legal capabilities to short-circuit the diplomatic channel should be established in order to try and keep up with the speed of the Internet.

References:

- ARMIN, J. 2008. McColo – Cyber Crime USA Report V2.0; Atrivo – Cyber Crime USA White Paper V1.0 [online]. [Accessed 01 September 2009]. Available from World Wide Web: http://hostexploit.com/index.php?option=com_content&view=article &id=12&Itemid=15.
- BACHFELD, D. 2008. Trojaner-Baukasten mit Rund-um-die-Uhr-Support und Austausch-Service [online]. [Accessed 01 September 2009]. Available from World Wide Web: http://www.heise.de/security/news/meldung/109254.
- BARROSO, D. 2007. Botnets – The Silent Threat. ENISA Position Paper No. 3 [online]. [Accessed 01 September 2009]. Available from World Wide Web: http://www.enisa.europa.eu/doc/pdf/deliverables/enisa_pp_botnets.pdf.
- BIZEUL, D. 2008. Russian Business Network study V1.0.1 [online]. [Accessed 01 September 2009]. Available from World Wide Web: http://www.bizeul.org/files/RBN_study.pdf.
- BOLDUAN, G. 2008. Digitaler Untergrund. Technology Review (Germany). 2008 (April), pp. 27 – 34.
- BSI (Bundesamt für Sicherheit in der Informationstechnik). 2009. Die Lage der IT-Sicherheit in Deutschland 2009 [online]. [Accessed 01 September 2009]. Available from World Wide Web: https://www.bsi.bund.de/cae/servlet/contentblob/476182/publication File/30715/Lagebericht2009_pdf.pdf.
- BUNDESVERFASSUNGSGERICHT. 2008. BVerfG, 1 BvR 370/07 vom 27.2.2008, [online]. [Accessed 08 September 2009]. Available from World Wide Web: http://www.bundesverfassungsgericht.de/entscheidungen/rs20080227_1bvr037007en.html.
- DEBREBANT, S. 2008. Der Ort, aus dem die Ebay-Betrüger kommen [online]. [Accessed 01 September 2009]. Available from World Wide Web: http://www.stern.de/digital/online/rumaenien-der-ort-aus-dem-die-ebay-betrueger-kommen- 607310.html.
- FABER, F. 2008. Unter Verdacht. c't. 2008 (11), pp. 92 – 96.
- FINJAN INC. 2009. Cybercrime Intelligence Report, Issue 2, 2009 [online]. [Accessed 01 September 2009]. Available from World Wide Web: http://www.finjan.com/Content. aspx?id=1367.
- FOSSI, M./BLACKBIRD, J./LAUCHT, M.P./JOHNSON, E./MCKINNEY, D./GOUGH, J./TURNER, D./LOW, M.K./MACK, T./ADAMS, T. 2008. Symantec Report on the Underground Economy [online]. [Accessed 01 September 2009]. Available from World Wide Web: http://eval.symantec.com/mktginfo/enterprise/white_papers/b-whitepaper_underground_economy_report_11-2008-14525717.en-us.pdf.
- HAYASHI, K. 2009. From Virtual Money to Real Money, [online]. [Accessed 01 September 2009]. Available from World Wide Web: http://www.symantec.com/ norton/antivirus-gaming/articles/details.jsp?aid=article_8.

- HERLEY, C./FLORÊNCIO, D. 2008. A Profitless Endeavour: Phishing as Tragedy of the Commons [online]. [Accessed 01 September 2009]. Available from World Wide Web: http://research.microsoft.com/en-us/um/people/cormac/Papers/PhishingAsTragedy.pdf.
- HOLZ, T./ZHUGE, J./HAN, X./GUO, J./ZOU, W. 2007. Characterizing the IRC-based Botnet Phenomenon [online]. [Accessed 01 September 2009]. Available from World Wide Web: http://honeyblog.org/junkyard/reports/botnet-china-TR.pdf.
- INTERNET CRIME COMPLAINT CENTER, 2005 – 2009. IC3 Annual Reports [online]. [Accessed 01 September 2009]. Available from World Wide Web: http://www.ic3.gov/media/annualreports.aspx.
- KREBS, B. 2007. Cyber-Criminals and Their Tools Getting Bolder, More Sophisticated [online]. [Accessed 01 September 2009]. Available from World Wide Web: http://www.washingtonpost.com/wpdyn/content/article/2007/03/13/AR2007031301522.html.
- MANSKE, M. 2007. Tatort Internet – eine globale Herausforderung für die Innere Sicherheit, BKA-Herbsttagung 2007 [online]. [Accessed 01 September 2009]. Available from World Wide Web: http://bka.de/kriminalwissenschaften/herbsttagung/2007/kurzfassung_manske.pdf.
- MELANI (MELDE- UND ANALYSESTELLE INFORMATIONSSICHERUNG, SWITZERLAND). 2008. Halbjahresbericht 2008/1 [online]. [Accessed 01 September 2009]. Available from World Wide Web: http://www.melani.admin.ch/dokumentation/00123/00124/01065/index.html?lang=de.
- MEYER-GOßNER, L., 2008. Strafprozessordnung. Munich: Beck.
- NAMESTNIKOV, Y. 2009. The Economics of Botnets [online]. [Accessed 01 September 2009]. Available from World Wide Web: http://www.viruslist.com/en/analysis?pubid=204792068.
- POULSEN, K. 2007. Fake Factoid Virus: 'Cybercrime More Lucrative Than Drug Trade' – Update [online]. [Accessed 01 September 2009]. Available from World Wide Web: http://www.wired.com/threatlevel/2007/09/cybercrime-more/.
- POULSEN, K. 2008. Cybercrime Supersite 'DarkMarket' Was FBI Sting, Documents Confirm [online]. [Accessed 01 September 2009]. Available from World Wide Web: http://www.wired.com/threatlevel/2008/10/darkmarket-post/.
- RIES, U. 2009. The fight against botnets is largely ineffective [online]. [Accessed 08 September 2009]. Available from World Wide Web: http://www.h-online.com/security/The-fight-against-botnets-is-largely-ineffective--/news/113146.
- SINGEL, R. 2009. Hackers Use Twitter to Control Botnet [online]. [Accessed 01 September 2009]. Available from World Wide Web: http://www.wired.com/threatlevel/2009/08/botnet-tweets/.
- STÅHLBERG, M. 2007. The Trojan Money Spinner [online]. [Accessed 01 September 2009]. Available from World Wide Web: http://www.f-secure.com/weblog/archives/VB2007_TheTrojanMoneySpinner.pdf.
- STONE-GROSS, B./COVA, M./CAVALLARO, L./GILBERT, B./SZYDLOWSKI, M./KEMMERER, R./KRUEGEL, C./VIGNA, G. 2009. Your Botnet is My Botnet: Analysis of a Botnet Takeover [online]. [Accessed 01 September 2009]. Available from World Wide Web: http://www.cs.ucsb.edu/~seclab/projects/torpig/torpig.pdf.

- THOMAS, R./MARTIN, J. 2006. The Underground Economy: Priceless [online]. [Accessed 01 September 2009]. Available from World Wide Web: http://usenix.org/publications/login/2006-12/openpdfs/cymru.pdf.
- URBANSKI, T. 2009. Heiße Ware: Handel mit Spiele-Accounts blüht, [online]. [Accessed 01 September 2009]. Available from World Wide Web: http://www.gdata.de/ueber-g-data/pressecenter/pressemeldungen/news-details/article/1303-heisse-ware-handel-mit-spiele.html.
- WIKIPEDIA, 2009. Cloud Computing [online]. [Accessed 08 September 2009]. Available from World Wide Web: http://en.wikipedia.org/w/index.php?title=Cloud_computing&oldid=312561007.
- WIKIPEDIA, 2009. Computer and Internet Protocol Address Verifier [online]. [Accessed 08 September 2009]. Available from World Wide Web: http://en.wikipedia.org/w/index.php?title=Computer_and_Internet_Protocol_Address_Verifier&oldid=296020129.
- ZETTER, K. 2007. I Was a Cybercrook for the FBI [online]. [Accessed 01 September 2009]. Available from World Wide Web: http://www.wired.com/politics/onlinerights/news/2007/01/72515

GERHARD SCHNEIDER

Consequences of Cloud Computing

Cloud Computing describes a new aspect of providing computing services to the masses. Only access to offered services via Internet is required, a service itself runs somewhere within the provider's infrastructure – which is perceived by the user as a cloud – and the result is returned via the Internet. Current marketing strategies only focus on the technological "no frills" approach. The fact that the provider has a full view of all user data is completely ignored as well as the fact that internationally operating providers are susceptible to different national legal strategies – and may be forced by the legal authorities of one country to move relevant data into their realm for inspection. Some of these hitherto undiscussed side effects of Cloud Computing will be addressed in this paper.

I. The Evolution of Cloud Computing

In the early days of computing, access to a computer required a dedicated terminal and an exclusive line, typically a telephone line or a special wire installation. The actual copper wires were visible to the user. Data was kept on the central machine, the mainframe, and a user was able to manipulate this data or to submit compute jobs. Literally everything happened on the mainframe. Early airline booking systems as well as the outdated German BTX system are good examples of this type of technology.

With the advent of the Internet, the need for special data lines vanished. New software on the client machine (typically a PC rather than a specialized terminal hardware) as well as communication protocols gave (and still give) the user the impression of a direct connection to the target computer. In fact data is sent over the Internet and various communication protocols make sure that the data stays correct and consistent and thus reaches its target unaltered. Remote access to computing facilities became a standard, leading to new working models like home offices. Early technical access solutions include *telnet* or *ssh* and nowadays server access via web browsers is probably the most common form.

Although the Internet was revolutionary in giving the user mobility, the basic view of a data centre remained unchanged. Company servers, hard disk storage and business software were still dominant and required both money and manpower to run an apparently complicated infrastructure.

Thus the next logical step was to look for computing resources accessible over the Internet, which gave rise to the idea of the Grid. Standardized access procedures ensure that access to large computing facilities becomes easy for the average user – as easy as the access to electricity via the power grid, thus the name for the concept. Rather than buying hardware, necessary resources can be bought on demand from some big computing site. This paradigm appears to be quite successful in the scientific area where researches run their own computing jobs on the largest supercomputers in the world.

The average user, however, does not need explicit hardware resources, but rather a service – a mail system that receives and stores email reliably or storage where a private collection of digital photographs can be deposited and retrieved at a later stage. These needs are addressed by Cloud Computing. Services rather than pure hardware access are offered to the end user and the service provider either runs his own hardware infrastructure or buys additional capacity on demand via the Grid infrastructure. Additional capacity is available as other providers may have to buy hardware to meet peak performance demands only, but their hardware is otherwise unused. The user no longer gets an idea about the underlying hardware infrastructure and thus views it as a (foggy) cloud – thus the word "Cloud" is used for this computing paradigm.

Amazon, for example, is a typical provider in the Cloud. They need large computing facilities to meet the Christmas demand and there is no alternative for them than to really run enough hardware: once Christmas is over, the related business opportunities are gone. During the rest of the year, the machines are idle, if not switched off, and thus additional money can be made by selling the computing time in the Grid or additional services in the Cloud.

In terms of economic success the idea of the Cloud seems to be more successful, as it is a lot easier to specify a service than a hardware resource.

To highlight the idea of the Cloud, it may be best to quote an example from the Amazon webpage (as of May 2009). Amazon charges 0.15€ for one GB per month, for the first 50 TB. Note that TB is no misprint, but highlights the scale in which business happens. Thus your personal 10GB for photos, etc, cost around 18€ per year or 90€ for 5 years. This compares nicely with both the cost and the life expectancy of a private 500 GB disk. But this price tag includes a full service, like backup, redundancy, invisible recovery procedures and optimal use of electric energy as well as permanent access from all over the world. The drawback is that transfer (both upload and download) costs extra. If the private 500GB disk crashes, which unfortunately sometimes happens, the service benefits of the Cloud are really appreciated.

Suppose a company needs 50TB of storage for a 5 month project – now. In the Amazon storage cloud this should amount to approximately 37,500€. A professional storage device for 50 TB is currently (July, 2009) around 27,000€, plus the cost of operation, staff, etc. Again the breakeven is visible, especially if the storage is definitely not required after the end of the project or the purchase generates a delay of, say, a month.

Google, for example, offers mail accounts with 2 GB storage for free, including world wide access, full service and a number of advanced features. Such offers are only possible as large systems scale much better and in a mail server with 100TB disk storage an individual user is no longer a cost issue. Yet the question arises why someone would give away resources for free, even if the cost is marginal.

II. Some Challenges of Cloud Computing

Scott McNealy, CEO of SUN Microsystems, once pointed out that one does no longer need to buy aeroplanes in order to operate an airline. It is enough to buy surplus capacity from the old fashioned airlines and resell it. But what happens, if resources are running low?

With respect to Cloud storage, it is probably safe to assume that there will not be sudden peaks in demand all over the world at the same time. Thus the Internet is an excellent means to retrieve capacity from where it is available, so that a moderate worldwide continuous growth can cope with local excess demands. The bigger challenge seems to be the access bandwidth. An easy calculation reveals that a standard DSL line is not suitable to transfer the 50 TB of the above example.

Many providers which operate in the Cloud are international companies. This raises the question which law applies when and where. After all the owner of data stored in the Cloud may live in one country while the data is physically stored on a server in a different country – and the provider may be located in a third country. The Cloud, however, does not reveal any insight into the real structure of a service for a user.

The author had the chance to question several vice presidents of large mail providers. It was always claimed that the email is kept totally secure. And of course the provider would adhere to any legal requests by a government like handing over the complete communication of a suspect. However, questions about the handling of US government or CIA requests related to private emails of non-US citizens were always met with silence or confusion.

During the 2009 German Federal Election, some parties were trying to raise money via PayPal. Since PayPal processes its data in the US, other countries may now have valuable information about the supporters of the German political system.

This highlights the greatest challenge of the Cloud paradigm: a service provider has complete access to all individual data and can move it physically around the world, without the user noticing it. The business model is no real protection. It is obvious that any abuse of data by Google, say, will immediately put them out of business, as nobody would want to trust them any longer. But data can be also moved onto a server in a country with "appropriate" legislation for inspection of the data by local government officials or perhaps to escape a search warrant in the original country.

Addressing this issue may seem paranoid at first, but the Cloud setup allows for an easy public execution of important people of perhaps a different country, since the provider can look at the data and tip someone off. Industrial espionage is another potential application of this scenario and cases of espionage by friendly countries are well known.

Thus it is not so much the question whether a Cloud provider can be a reliable partner in technical terms, but whether he is allowed to be reliable in legal terms. This comes from the fact that Cloud providers have left the boundaries and safe havens of classical national legislation.

III. User Self Defense

There is no obvious legal solution for this issue, given the diversity of societies in the world. Thus the only way from the user perspective is to only store data in the cloud which is useless for anybody else, including the provider, using encryption. While this seems to be easier for storage of raw data, encryption of email on the provider servers is more difficult to handle.

In addition it raises the question who should develop the necessary encryption programs. Neither the provider nor a government sponsored institution seem to be a good choice to protect a citizen from the curiosity of friendly states. After all, the TSA approved luggage locks are a perfect example of total insecurity.

There are a few nice solutions available. For example the TeamDrive product (www.teamdrive.net) only stores encrypted files in the Cloud. The encryption works without the Cloud provider and apparently also without the software company. It provides automatic synchronisation over several computers via the Cloud and realises the model of a shared online/offline workspace. Note that this is no advertising of a product nor a warranty for the cryptographic validity of the approach, but merely a hint that steps are being made in the right direction.

IV. Challenges revisited

A number of issues arise with respect to cloud computing which were unknown in the old localized computing models:

- Who is monitoring the network? The network operator may also see the data while it is transferred onto a server in the Cloud or moved from one server to another.
- Where is the physical storage of the data?
- Who operates the computers where the services are running? The operator may modify a computer so that job execution may be incorrect.
- Where are the jobs being run? This can be a challenge for the user as well as for the provider, if, say, the purpose of the computation is illegal at the server site, but completely legal in the user's home country.

- Who monitors your jobs? Even if the computer running a job is under the same legal framework as the owner of the job, monitoring the jobs from abroad (e.g. via 'offshoring') may give valuable insight into the planned activities.
- Who keeps the backup of the data? As any reliable server site will run backup procedures, personal data may still be available to the provider even after the original data has been deleted.

A simple service may now be distributed all over the world, with different server sites contributing to the service. Each site may be unable to provide the service on its own, but different laws apply at each site.

The simple answer "do not use Cloud services" will not solve the issue in a modern fast moving IT world. Thus at least both understanding and acceptance of user counter measures are required, even if they reduce the power of local authorities.

The Cloud service provider faces similar challenges: suppose a user is running a simulation program to improve a nuclear bomb. While this may be legal for a US citizen on a US server, this may not be the case for a user of a different nationality. The provider cannot determine the purpose of compiled computer programs but may bear a responsibility.

Certain users may use Cloud storage to share (encrypted) pornographic material, others may use the surplus of available machines to send SPAM messages or carry out denial of service attacks of hitherto unknown dimensions.

Even if the Cloud service provider may not be liable, he will be under public pressure. In self defense the provider will try to keep all data (including connection data) forever so that the blame can be shifted from the provider to the misbehaving user. The provider may also choose to permanently check the user data, both manually and in an automated way. Since services are offered – unlike the Internet, which supplies mere connectivity – it may be possible to understand and interpret the data.

Thus the more pressure is put onto the provider, e.g. via liability issues, the more likely user privacy is at stake.

V. Consequences for data centres and for society

Even the computer centre of the University of Freiburg is running a (small) Cloud environment, within the state legal framework. Thus local users seem to be safe – at first sight.

Nevertheless it seems that too much data is collected about each user, because of legislation or University rules to prevent fraud, because of professional code of conduct and by hardware manufacturers who require error logs.

The combination of all this data is interesting – and the more one has the more information can be retrieved by cross-linking the various pieces of data.

The idea to move the relevant data to a trusted government site to ease the burden of the local institution just moves the problem and makes it bigger because central sites accumulate even more data for potential cross-linking.

There is a wide spread misconception, especially among legal professionals, that it is possible to hide in the enormous "sea of data." This underestimates the power of modern computers. The latest server at the University computing centre holds 8 CPUs and 512 GB of memory. This is enough to store 80 Bytes for every human on earth in the fast main memory of the machine. Cross-searches across the whole human population are quite easy today. The cost of such a machine is not prohibitive, with a mere 40,000€ (December 2008).

Therefore we see the need for an accepted set of new ethics for IT management, which will then lead to appropriate legislation which has to be accepted by the public – even if it contradicts short-sighted security demands.

One corner stone will have to be a guaranteed anonymity, even if certain abuses can no longer be identified. The unsolved murder cases suggest that society is willing to accept such anonymity in the real world, even at that high price.

The greed to store all sorts of data to keep traces will have to be controlled; in fact it has to be accepted that such data should not be stored or at least it should be deleted as soon as possible. Although cars are being used for bank robberies, nobody has suggested to permanently track all cars and to store their tracks for years – just in case.

Data centres will have to learn that data which a user explicitly wants to delete must be deleted immediately, including the backups and other traces. Nobody has asked the paper industry to provide automated carbon copies, in case the user loses or burns the original. Yet the IT industry still seems to believe in the incompetent user who deletes files without knowing what he or she is doing.

Finally, society will have to learn not to use data sets, which happen to be available, for other previously unintended purposes. The German Toll Collect system serves as a perfect example. Although the German Parliament was quite aware of the potential control functions of the system and thus passed legislation that the data must only be used to track payments and for nothing else, other government institutions wanted the data for their purposes only a few days after the system became operational. The public will have to learn that unintended use may shatter confidence in any system and may change the behaviour of people.

However it seems that currently the development is moving into the opposite direction. A High Court in Germany recently ruled (BGH, Az. 1 StR 76/09) that email can easily be confiscated at the provider servers, while privacy laws apply once the mail has been downloaded onto the home computer. The application of the classical Post Office model – where letters can be confiscated by the police as long as the letter is not in the private letter box – completely ignores the aspects of Cloud computing. On the contrary it ensures that servers in the Cloud cannot respect privacy. A user who wants privacy, for whatever reason, will now have to ask the provider about deletion of all backups, once the mail is downloaded onto the private machine.

VI. Summary

The classical regulatory approach will not solve the issues arising from the Cloud paradigm, as this is set in an international framework. IT-professionals cannot control the use of the abundance of "useful" data, where a significant amount of the "useful" data is generated by legal requirements. Recent examples have shown that the legal system is also unable to restrict abuses. Apart from a new generally accepted guide of conduct the only real solution seems to be to generate less "useful" data and to accept the price of knowing less – it seems to be worth it.

Reference

BGH, Az. 1 StR 76/09 „http://juris.bundesgerichtshof.de/cgi-bin/rechtsprechung/document.py?Gericht=bgh&Art=en&Datum=2009-3&nr=47839&pos=0&anz=304&Blank=1.pdf"

KATALIN PARTI

Alterations in Danger-Awareness due to the Infocommunication Revolution and its Effect on Legislation

The study gives a brief introduction of what I call infocommunication revolution. The latest infocommunication development that came along with the Internet is different from the earlier ones (verbal communication, written communication, and mass printing). Secondly, the article embraces how the digital technology changed human thinking about the notion of "danger". For explaining this, I recall online child pornography cases and their appearance in the media and international legislative issues. Media displays and interprets these cases scandal-focused and hence, produces moral panic and false danger-awareness. It reflects not only in the general thinking of everyday people, but also in current international legislative issues. The study's central questions are: Do these alterations in general thinking base on reality or fiction (current trends)?; Could and might legal efforts be successful to stop increasing moral decay (future forecast)?; Can media be effective in repressing the idea of over-criminalization when its original goal is to suck and tie masses of people (futuristic and utopistic aspects)?

Due to the infocommunication revolutions people's thinking as regards danger has changed. The flow of information has become faster with every information revolution, and as a result, people are getting to have a more tangible feeling of danger. The change in the perception of danger is fundamentally triggered by the real and perceived beliefs on the decline of morals, which were also strengthened by the infocommunication revolutions. In my presentation, I wish to analyse the elements, sources, and effects on legislation of the moral panic caused by the the last information revolution, the appearance of the Internet.

I. An introduction to infocommunication revolutions

In my understanding, humanity was witness to four infocommunication revolutions (hereinafter referred to as IR). The first was the development of *speech*, parallel to the organisation into communities and the division of work. The newly formed speech enabled man to think in terms of concepts, and to abstract and generalise. A prerequisite of these were the organisation of communities, the use of tools and the division of work. The accomplishment of this first IR is to be found in the creation of symbols: it presented itself in the use of linguistic symbols and made it possible for man to refer to things that can not be seen, cannot be experienced or are not present at the given moment. When communities outgrew their primitive boundaries, the need arose to „store" information in a durable manner, mainly for commercial purposes. This brought on the second IR, the appearance of *writing*. Writing formed out of the drawing of simple ideograms, which initially denoted single objects or activities. The symbols then became increasingly abstract, and finally developed into symbols that are seemingly no more related to the original entity they used to symbolise. In the course of history, images slowly transformed into symbols, then letters, which make up nowadays' alphabets for the written representation of sounds. The third great leap was the invention of *printing*. With this new technology, knowledge became available to larger masses within a relatively short period of time from the mid-15th century. The fourth IR, that is the revolution of the *WWW and computers linked into networks*, that we can also witness today, was preceded by the dynamic development of telecommunication technology, namely the invention of the telegram and the telephone.

These devices made remote interactive information faster, and are therefore – in terms of function – the forerunners of the Internet (see Tivadar Puskás' exchange, then telephone news service (1893).) The Internet is however more than the previously mentioned media, in that it converges them. Digital convergence means (Polyák, 2002; Sallai, 2004; Koppányi, 2004) that the Internet unites in itself attributes that were formerly only possible to realise separately: through telecommunication (post, telephone, telefax etc.), and traditional media (press, radio, television). The attributes Internet unites and converges (1) data processing (digitisation role), (2) data transfer (supplying and forwarding role), and (3) content generation and transmission (medium role). This convergence is based on the fact that the above mentioned actors in telecommunication (telecom service providers and the media) used the same technology, the digitisation of data to fulfil their task. The Internet however makes it possible for any data to be generated in or transformed into a binary format, and to be transmitted in that format with the help of or to potentially any electronic communication device (e.g. internet surfing or watching TV screenings on cellphones). The tasks that were earlier the business of different service providers are covered now by one – the Internet.

The novelty of the WWW is that it is theoretically accessible from any place in the world. (However, the Internet as the medium that connects the world is a mere fiction, simply because while on poorer continents only a fraction of the population participates actively in Internet traffic e.g. 2.3% in Africa, and 5.5% in Central and Southern Asia, nearly 70% of the population in more developed regions, such as North America, Australia and Scandinavia regularly benefit from the blessings of the Internet.)[1]

The WWW also provides unlimited storage capacity: the Internet is an unlimited knowledge base that can be further extended to any depth. This extension solely depends on the future development of broadband technologies.

---

[1] Source: http://www.kwintessential.co.uk/map/internet-penetration.html

Perhaps the most apparent novelty of the Internet lies in its personalisability. The users themselves can influence the creation and shaping of Internet content, while traditional media only publishes selected information, and offers opportunities for its passive reception (e.g. the above mentioned telephone news service, radio, television). Individual users can however shape the Internet to their liking, and only browse for and make available to others such content that they themselves prefer. As a consequence, it is primarily not the preferences of the administrators of the media (such as the government, television corporations etc.), but the users' needs that define the development of Internet technologies and content.

II. Aversions towards the infocommunication revolutions. Moral panic as the *sine qua non* of the infocommunication revolution

The IRs also gave rise to negative critique that drew the public's attention to the socially destructive effects – mainly the loosening morals – of the given medium, and on these grounds attempted to curb the further ripples of the IR.

The most important concerns were related to the shift in paradigms. The church's fears of loosing their monopoly for knowledge – that were first raised by the invention of printing and the conquest against analphabetism – were very much founded. Voices that prophesied that expansion of knowledge and the rapid spread of revolutionary ideas further fuelled these fears. Mentioning just one of these revolutionary happenings, greater masses were introduced to the teachings of Luther by the advent of printing, which is exactly when the ideas of reformation started to spread and the hegemony of the Catholic church gradually came to an end.

Partly similar worries related to the quality of the body of information to be found on the Internet arise today. They say that the knowledge on the Internet is not "clean", not reliable, and often even its source can not be traced back. By the fact that anybody may upload content to the Internet, there is no unified and reliable body of knowledge online. Contents are diluted due to personalisation, and their quality declines. News centres earlier considered to be objective, but now offer an increasingly shallow quality of content. The latest example for that is the *mass wire media*. Mass wire media is one of the most popular reporting techniques of the high-tech age, which involves users, radio and television audiences, and even people walking in the street reporting on the events going on around them, which almost immediately appears in traditional mass media – radio or television – or the Internet (such a mass wire medium is e.g. CNN iReport). Its defining feature is that people may create and edit news that they believe to be important. It is also important that these reports are real-time – the news are not generated after the event, but rather at the same time –, and subjectivity – the reporter selects what he wants to talk about, what he wants to "publish" – which makes news more exact and user-oriented, but also more subjective. This latter feature is a negative critique, because a subjective view-point can make news misleading. This newest form of mass communication is called *Social Media Revolution.*

It is also thanks to the IRs that communities of scientists are now somewhat more formed (as a contrast to the earlier ages when scientists tended to be rather isolated), they founded organisations, which made the publication and systematisation of discoveries and scientific findings easier. As a consequence there is no need any more for human communities to develop the different inventions individually, because the world opened up, hence scientific findings spread quickly and became available almost immediately everywhere int he world. IRs speeded up the development and perfection of the existing results (e.g. this is how Tivadar Puskás gained access to the telephone invented by Bell which he developed further: he invented the telephone news service that delivered the latest news to great masses at affordable prices).

Today, we can still witness the worries related to traditional methods of education becoming inappropriate. While as a result of printing, man moved away from a metaphorical, but simplified, image-based thinking towards accepting the scientific approach (more exact formulation, authentic, reliable knowledge),[2] this process is now reversed with the appearance of the Internet. While educators have to strive to have the gist of the information appear on one single page, image-based thinking is once more pushed to the foreground. On the one hand, this is conducive to the development of metaphorical, abstract thinking and associative skills, but many believe that what we gain on the swings, we lose on the roundabouts: the varied nature and great amount of information dilutes the content down, and there is no guarantee that the student will use the right source to extend his knowledge. Therefore, it was not only the spread of books that transformed teaching methods – as we moved away from lecture-based teaching towards learning based on the independent perception of knowledge –, but the Internet also has a similar effect. Internet-use is coming to the foreground in education, first only as an aid, a source of supplementary knowledge, then gradually as a tool of independent learning: distance learning appears. There are worries concerning the role of the teachers becoming void, and the survival and competitiveness of the traditional *universitas*.[3] The worries not only concern the loss of a unified method, but also the loss of a unified – and reliable – knowledge.

Worries related to the devaluation of books emerged both in connection with printing and the spread of the Internet. Noblemen used to banish printed books

---

[2] According to McLuhan, Eisenstein, Kittler and Giesecke, printing brought on the „monopoly of writing" which took on the earlier role of images in society.

[3] Still, Mark Y. Herring (the Dean of Winthrop University) lists 10 reasons why the Internet and digital media can not replace libraries of printed books. (Herring, 2001)

from their libraries for fear that they might devaluate their rare, hand-copied books. But the appearance of the Internet and the digitisation of information dealt the final blow to books as artworks.

The appearance of the Internet also gave rise to several new concerns, never witnessed before in the history of IRs.

Concerns related to the infringement of personal rights, constitutional rights and intellectual property rights specifically arose with the spread of the Internet. Whole personality profiles can be drawn up by gathering personal information uploaded to community sites, which offer an excellent opportunity for abuse (identity theft). The tools of protection against harmful Internet content – filtering softwares – are not sufficiently developed to provide actual protection for children. The blocking (making inaccessible) of any content deemed to be harmful by the governments (e.g. in Cuba or China, see Timofeeva, 2006) is unimaginable in any constitutional democracy, as it would prejudice the right of free access to information, and the freedom of speech, opinions and conscience. Several authors have until today not given their consent to the digitisation of their works for fear they might be devaluated, but a loss of copyright fees is also a realistic threat.[4]

The other aspect of the worries related to the Internet involves the possible, and up to now unknown effects of this new medium on the personality. Certain philosophies fear that too much information may lead to a distortion of the personality. According to the *fragmentation* theory (Hitzler & Honer, 1994; McLuhan, 1995),[5] there is too much information on the Internet from cultures unknown to the individual. The individual is incapable of incorporating this huge body of information into his own socialisation environment, as a result of which the presonality breaks down – gets fragmented – and then the individual builds up a new personality using information from the Internet that he prefers. He may form new habits, new behavioural elements, and a new personality, which are not always supported by the cultural environment of the individual. This may lead to the social exclusion of the individual. Personalities formed this way are cast out by society or the community, the individual falls into depression, may commit suicide, or lose his or her identity and behavioural patterns. The mass exclusion of individuals leads to a general crisis of values, or may deepen the already existing one.

Further aversions towards cyber-communities are born out of the threat of emerging cyber-deviances. A cyber-deviance in general means the adjustment to the online environment coupled with double moral standards. Double moral standard (Michelet, 2003: 16) means that the majority of users traditionally respects

[4] You could still build a brilliant collection of the books that remain off-line, e.g. "Harry Potter" series; "Catcher in the Rye"; "Catch-22"; "Lolita"; "To Kill a Mockingbird"; "Atlas Shrugged"; "Things Fall Apart"; "The Outsiders" and "Fahrenheit 451"

[5] See also cultural identity theory. (Erikson, 2002)

accepted norms, but in online communities they live by different standards (e.g. they would not steal a mobile phone or a bag etc. but they have no qualms about downloading copyrighted software from the Internet, which is also illegal). These double moral standards are nourished by people's faith in anonimity, that is the belief that the parties communicating online are „invisible" or unidentifiable.

The feeling of „invisibility" leads to unscrupulous behaviour. According to psychologists these concerns first emerge in relation to online communities that have reached a certain developmental status, namely the virtual realities (e.g. Second Life, The Sims Online). Virtual realities create new personalities. In virtual realities, the individual is not physically present, but is represented by an alterego (avatar) that does not obviously mirror the original characteristics of its creator. Alteregos may turn to new methods of problem-solving. These methods might be unacceptable in a society based on traditional norms, e.g. causing psychological or physical harm to other alteregos. Psychologists (Ritter et al., 2004) and criminologists (Rogers, 2001; Rátai, 2005; Clement, 2000) say that the participation in the life of virtual realities based on deviant standards may cause especially serious distortions in the personality of children.

Some social scientists even claim that the spread of online communication leads to the complete decline of existing moral values. The reason for this is the mass appearance of harmful contents on the Internet and their availability by anyone, especially youngsters. Such contents – like pornography, xenophobia, incitement to hatred or extremist ideas – were not available to anyone before the Internet age and were very difficult to spread. As by now everbody can potentially access these materials, they are becoming increasingly extreme due to the competition. Through the example of pornography, this can be illustrated as follows:

When?	The audience of pornography	General opinion on pornography	Social attitude
Before the Internet	Targeted groups: marketeers, black market, news agents, buyers of erotic literature, visitors of video rental shops	"Extreme"	Excluding, rejecting
After the appearance and spread of the Internet	Groups are not specifically targeted: everybody with an internet connection	"Ordinary"	Tolerant, accepting

Table: The transformation of pornography with the appearance of the Internet

III. The triggers of moral panic and its reverberations in legislation

The major threat in relation to the infocommunication revolutions was thought to be slipping morals. For this reason, initially only the negative effects of all new revolutionary media were emphasised.

But overemphasising the negative effects is basically creation of the panic. This is where the responsibility of traditional media shows (I refer to the press, radio, and television as traditional media, which offer pre-filtered contents to the audiences). The true catalyst of moral panic is the traditional media, which partly by the very principles of their operation, enhance the panic effect. Only shocking, scandalous or scary information has any newsworthiness. These media present such information in a pre-filtered manner, lifted out of the original context. (Programmes that expressly emphasise the *fact* of downfall of morals, of the crisis of values and of the moral crisis further add to this.)

The following cases offer a good example to how the traditional media regard "newsworthy" information. I picked cases, where the Internet is specifically made responsible for the onset of the moral crisis.

A new habit is spreading among youngsters surfing the Internet: they post erotic images of themselves to community sites with increasing regularity. Experts say that already primary school children aged 11 to 12, early in adolescence, post such images to the world wide web. Boys are photographed bare-chested, and girls in provocative clothes and poses, so that they appear more adult.

Kamaszdivat az internetes kitárulkozás [Posing on the Internet is in fashion among adolescents] (szexting) – Népszabadság Online, 2009

A decision by a number of UK internet providers to block a Wikipedia page showing an image of a naked girl has angered users of the popular site. (...) The IWF said it was a "potentially illegal child sexual abuse image". (...) Some volunteers argued that the image was available in a number of books and had never been ruled illegal.

About the Scorpions' 1977s album depicting a girl naked, BBC News, 2008

How would people act if they were freed from real life laws and social constraints? A new, interactive computer game offers just such a scenario – with some disturbing results. Mr Ludlow (an academic philosopher, also a player) thought the people behind the game should know what was going on inside Alphaville, not least because some things – child prostitution, for example – are morally and legally troubling. But when they found out, Maxis, the game's developers, and Electronic Arts, the distributors, banned all in-game mention of The Alphaville Herald. Then, says Mr Ludlow, he was thrown out of the game and his accounts closed down, cutting him off from his Sims.

One of the first anxious news about virtual realities; this time about The Sims Online, BBC News, 2003

Second Life[6] *is being investigated by German police following allegations that some members are trading child abuse images in the online world. The investigation follows a report by a German TV news programme which uncovered the trading group and members who pay for sex with virtual children."*

BBC News, 2007

A Chinese software developer was arrested by authorities for developing an online sex game. The authorities claimed that the game contained illegal, pornographic content, and the developer also benefited from it. According to the spokesman of the Chinese ministry for public security, the game had more than 200,000 registered users, and about 700 paying members. The enterprise was started in March 2007 under the name „The hut of girlfriends", and brought the developer profits of approx. 30 thousand yuan (730 thousand HUF, about 2,433 EUR).

Origo, 2007

Apple Inc. *is apologizing for allowing a 99-cent* iPhone *game called "Baby Shaker" that let a player quiet a virtual crying infant by shaking the device. The game asked players to see how long they could endure a baby's cries and then shake the phone to stop the wailing.* Apple *removed the program from the iPhone's App Store on Wednesday, but critics pressed for an apology Thursday. Apple spokeswoman Natalie Kerris said that the game was "deeply offensive" and said it should not have been approved for sale.*

Yahoo Tech News, 2009 April

However, not only media news create panic. Scientific research on changes of behaviour in relation to the new medium, the Internet, can also fuel moral panic. Science may be objective in its principles, but it still can not explain a lot of phenomena, or predict their effects (see e.g. what an effect the presence in a virtual reality community may have on the personality), and in such cases resorts to the method of guessing when looking for arguments and consequences.

Legislation on the new medium – even though only indirectly – also contributes to the deepening of the moral panic. Legislation is always based on scientific research and consultation with experts, but it can not shake off the effect of politics either. Political interests always try to ensure that public opinion prevails, and are certainly under pressure from the public opinion. For this reason, legislation also can not remain completely unaffected by the moral trends triggered by the feeling of panic. (See diagram on the next page)

[6] Second Life invented and created by Linden Laboratory Inc. California is a virtual roleplay space on internet. As its name implies, it is a virtual world in which members create an avatar and then use that character to live out a separate existence. Hasonló második valóságok: The Sims Online, Alphaville City

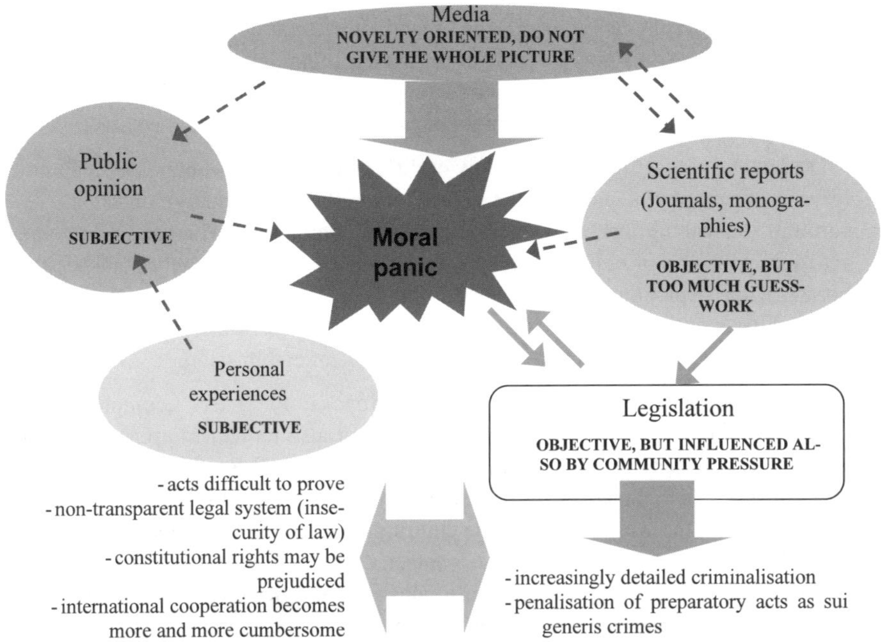

Diagram: The triggers of moral panic and its reverberations in legislation

Legislation trends in recent times point to the penalisation of an ever wider circle of acts, the criminalisation of preparatory acts, and the exaggerated regulation of details. The most recent examples for these are the European Council's Convention on Cybercrime adopted on 23 November 2001 (hereinafter Cybercrime Convention),[7] Council Framework Decision 2004/68/JHA of 22 December 2003 on combating the sexual exploitation of children and child pornography (hereinfater Framework Decision), the Council of Europe Convention on the Protection of children against sexual exploitation and sexual abuse adopted on 27 October 2008 in Lanzarote[8] (hereinafter Lanzarote convention), and the recommendation of the Committee on Civil Liberties, Justice and Home Affairs to the EP (hereinafter 2009 proposal for a EP recommendation).[9]

---

[7] Convention on Cybercime, CETS. No. 185 – 23.XI.2001. See online: http://conventions.coe.int

[8] Council of Europe Convention on the Protection of children against sexual exploitation and sexual abuse. CETS. No. 201 – 25. X. 2007. See online: http://conventions.coe.int

[9] Committee on Civil Liberties, Justice and Home Affairs' report with a proposal for a European Parliament recommendation to the Council on combating the sexual exploitation of children and child pornography (2008/2144(INI)) 26.01.2009; see also: European Parliament recommendation of 3 February 2009 to the Council on combating the sexual ex-

The Cybercrime Convention and the Framework Decision regard all depictions of child pornography as criminal. The objects of commission do not only include depictions of existing minors engaged in sexually explicit conduct, but realistic images representing a minor engaged in sexually explicit conduct, and also depictions of persons appearing to be a minor engaged in sexually explicit conduct.[10]

Despite the above, the applicable law of different countries is not unified: not only visual or graphic depictions, but textual descriptions (Germany), and voice recordings (answering machines) can be an act of commission. Hungary, where the act of commission of child pornogaphy has a narrow definition only punishes the pornographic depiction of *existing* minors. At the same time, mainly in the youngest member states of the EU, such as Slovenia, Romania or Bulgaria, there is no clearly delineated legal practice concerning the acts of commission.

The Lanzarote convention and the 2009 proposal for a EP recommendation would not only regard the actual sexual abuse, but also its related preparatory behaviours as sui generis criminal acts. Such a behaviour is for example an online chat session with the intention of sexual exploitation, or any other forms of contacting children online with the aim of the child's sexual abuse.[11] The question is, how it can be evidenced that the child was contacted online in preparation of an actual act of abuse offline, if the actual abuse does not take place (or at least does not start). (Independent of that, the deceitful nature of the preparatory behaviour could be assessed as part of the deliberation of the sentence.)

The Lanzarote convention extends the scope of punishable preparatory behaviours, e.g. the access – without downloading – of websites containing child pornography.[12] Here, however, a question of proof arises, namely how to distinguish technically between intentional downloading and unintentional access. At the moment, the fact that the perpetrator did not „access" the child pornography contents out of negligence but intentionally can only be proven with indirect evidence. Such indirect evidence may be for instance the magnitude of further child pornography content recovered from the computer of the accusee, their classification into galleries, or whether the accusee visited websites containing child pornography often or not. (Krone, 2004; Krone 2005) By any means, a proof of intentional access beyond any doubt is at the moment technically not feasible.

The 2009 proposal for a EP recommendation would regard all persons „serving" Internet users showing an interest in child abuse as criminal, among them also those operating online chatrooms and forums dealing with sexual exploitation of children. The question remains, however, which chatrooms can be proven to be aimed at the sexual exploitation

ploitation of children and child pornography (2008/2144(INI)) See online: http://www.europarl.europa.eu

[10] Article 9 Paragraph 2 of the Cybercrime Convention; Article 1 paragraph b./ of the Framework decision

[11] Article 23 of the Lanzarote convention

[12] Paragraph 1.f/ of Article 20 of the Lanzarote convention

of children. Is it sufficient for example for someone to initiate such a conversation in a chatroom and not to be expelled from the chatroom, or will it be only chatrooms with conversations exlusively of such nature that meet the criteria, or will there have to be such a chatroom service affiliated with a website containing child pornography content?

IV. Conclusion

The above mentioned legislative trends are influenced by the concerns communicated by the traditional media, the need for the protection of citizens (children), and the findings of scientific research. Therefore, legislation is shifting towards a detailed regulation which carries the following risks:

- There is a trap of detail-regulation, casuistic decisions, redundancy, overregulation and lack of transparency.
- There is also a troublesome tendency of criminalising preparatory behaviours, the fact that these are difficult to prove, and it is difficult to separate intentionality from negligence.
- Due to overcriminalisation, criminal law becomes *prima ratio* instead of *ultima ratio*. Criminal law becomes the tool of primary reaction to milder deviances as well. This is a dangerous trend, especially if it is not coupled with other preventive tools, as information on safe Internet-use is scarce, and even parents are unaware of how they could prepare their children for the dangers of Internet-use. (Michelet, 2003; Mitchell et al., 2003; Kiesler et al., 2000; Turow & Nir, 2000)
- It has to be defined with great care what contents we consider to be harmful to youngsters, because if we define an overly inclusive scope, consitutional rights may be prejudiced (e.g. freedom of opinion, right of access to information).

Works consulted

- CLEMENT, A. (2000). Research paper: Social implications of current trends in information / communication technologies. Strategic Issues Series rp02-9e University of Toronto, 2000
- ERIKSON, E.H. (2002). Gyermekkor és társadalom. [Childhood and society] Osiris, Budapest
- HERRING, M.Y. (2001). 10 reasons why the Internet is no substitute for a library. Könyvtári Figyelő. Vol. 47, issue 2001/4 also American Libraries, April 2001, pp. 76-78.
- HITZLER, R. & HONER, A. (1994). Bastelexistenz. Über subjektive Konsequenzen der Individuaisierung. In: U. Beck (ed.): Riskante Freiheiten. Frankfurt/M: Beck-Gernsheim, 1994 Quoted by Malinák, 2005
- KIESLER, S., ZDANIUK, B., LUNDMARK, V. & KRAUT, R. (2000). Troubles with the Internet: The dynamics of help at home. Human-Computer Interaction, 15(4), 323-351

- KOPPÁNYI SZ. (2004). A szabályozói konvergencia helyzete és lehetséges irányai a mai Magyarországon. (előadás) [Situation of regulatory convergence and its possible directions in Hungary today; lecture] „A médiakonvergencia előrehaladása és hatása a magyar médiaszabályozásra" konferencia [conference on The progress of media convergence and it effect in Hungarian media regulations], Széchenyi István University, Győr, 16 July 2004
- KRONE, T. (2004). A Typology of Online Child Pornography Offending. Trends and Issues in Crime and Criminal Justice, Canberra: Australian Institute of Criminology. No. 279 June 2004, http://www.aic.gov.au/publications/tandi2/tandi279.pdf
- KRONE, T. (2005). Does Thinking Make it so? Defining Online Child Pornography Possession Offences. Trends and Issues in Crime and Criminal Justice. Canberra: Australian High Tech Crime Centre, No. 299 April 2005 p. 1-6
- MALINÁK J. (2005). Az egyéni identitás létrejötte a médiakultúra globalizálódásának kontextusában (PhD értekezés) [Creating self identity in the context of globalisation of media culture (PhD dissertation)] PTE BTK Irodalomtudományi Doktori Iskola Kultúratudományi Doktori Program http://www.szinhaz.hu/edan/PhD/studenttexts/malinak_judit.htm
- MCLUHAN, M. (1995). Understanding media. The Extension of Man. New York: The MIT Press
- MICHELET, I. (2003). Our Children at Risk Online: The Example of Thailand. ECPAT International
- MITCHELL, K.J., FINKELHOR, D. & WOLAK, J. (2003). The Exposure Of Youth To Unwanted Sexual Material On The Internet. A National Survey of Risk, Impact, and Prevention Youth & Society, Vol. 34, No. 3 pp. 330-358
- POLYÁK G. (2002). Hatalom-leosztás. Önszabályozás az Interneten. [Distribution of power. Self-regulation on the Internet] Jogi Fórum Online [Legal Forum Online]: http://www.jogiforum.hu/publikaciok/63
- RÁTAI B. (2005). Virtuális jelenlét és virtuális világok. [Virtual presence and virtual worlds] In: Dömölki, B., Kósa, Zs., Kömlődi, F. & Rátai, B.: Az információs társadalom technológiai távlatai. Tanulmány. [The technological prospects of the information society; study] Nemzeti Hírközlési és Informatikai Tanács [National Council for Communications and Information Technology] September 2005. http://www.nhit-it3.hu/it3-cd/13.Virtualis_jelenlet_es_virtualis_vilagok.pdf
- RITTER A., FÁBIÁN ZS., PILLÓK P. & HOYER M. (2004). Felmérés a magyarországi internet-használatról: betegség, vagy korosztályra jellemző tünet? [An assessment of Hungarian Internet-use: Illness, or an age-related symptom?] Psychiatria Hungarica 2004, 19: 131-140
- ROGERS, M.K. (2001). A social learning theory and moral disengagement analysis of criminal computer behavior: An exploratory Study. UMI Dissertation Services pp. 57-58
- SALLAI Gy. (2004). A távközlés, az informatika és a média konvergenciája. (előadás) [The convergence of telecommunication, information technology and media; lecture] „A médiakonvergencia előrehaladása és hatása a magyar médiaszabályozásra" konferencia [conference on The progress of media convergence and its effect on Hungarian media regulations], Széchenyi István University, Győr, 16 July 2004
- TIMOFEEVA, Y. (2006). Censorship in Cyberspace. New Regulatory Strategies in the Digital Age on the Example of Freedom of Expression. Nomos
- TUROW, J. & NIR, L. (2000). The Internet and the family 2000: The view from parents, the view from kids. Philadelphia: University of Pennsylvania, Annenberg Public Policy Center

Meinrad Rombach

Layperson's Responsibility for IT Security

How to support the crowd of security actors

The human factor is well known as a major IT security loophole. Any concept for corporate security includes a TOP-down approach, where "TOP" stands for the three pillar model: Technology - Organisation - Personnel. In big corporations, a hierarchy of responsibilities is built from a CIO´s strategic insight down to each worker's liability to be aware of security issues affecting their particular workplace. Regarding smaller companies, the distribution of professional security knowledge turns poor. Very often, executives hand over their responsibility for company survival into the hands of external providers for IT technology, who can't handle a TOP concept's O and P parts efficiently. Many IT users (including executives) think of IT security as a technical matter of virus scanners and other black boxes with "built-in security", ignoring the need for a personal change in behaviour and lifelong learning. In small companies, IT administrators often concentrate on keeping the infrastructure running while doing a security side job with no time to act as a security officer appropriately. The Conficker worm's attack vector "USB-port" is an actual example of how the threatening situation did change in the last years towards men-machine interaction to be kept safe, while the technical pillar looses strength. Today's challenge is how to instruct and support liable laypersons to bring TOP security down to other laypersons in their network.

I. The Death of the Professional IT Generalist

Human skills and expert knowledge show a trend towards specialization and niche building driven by the increasing complexity of the information age. In the last century, it was convenient for professional workers to get an intensive vocational training followed by climbing the skill ladder of practise up to the level of professional mastery. The acquired practical experience was sufficient for a whole worker's life. Many professions could be well done by generalists having skills to cover each problem arising on thc job.

Today, the paradigm of "lifelong learning" did become reality in most of the working fields. The skill ladder started to sink into the weak ground, requiring a continued climbing in order to stay on an appropriate level of relevant knowledge. This introduced a new type of professional mastery, the specialist. With increasing speed, many professions had to focus more and more on staying up to date with the most important professional tasks they have to master on the job.

A. Who is a Layperson?

In this rise of specializing professional expertise, the professional impact of laypersons is increasing too. Everybody is acting as a layperson in all those topics he/she is not specialized for, but has to deal with. This applies for those fields, where he/she is not

- practising periodically
- aiming for professional mastery
- willing to update skills permanently

Today's "skill ladder climbing" requirements do imply layperson status for areas of

- minor personal interest
- lower visibility in the daily routine
- major changes in demands or requests

Bearing in mind all the different landscapes of IT, the label "IT specialist" looks almost undefined, because nobody can claim to concentrate the personal skill building on each IT topic.

The more areas that can't be covered professionally by an appropriate specialist, the more work has to be done by laypersons. The strong requirement to focus on certain topics throws into question, who is responsible for covering all the other problems not being focused on by a dedicated specialist.

B. IT Security in the Hands of Layperson Circles

A quick survey in the audience of this congress gave the impressive result that none of the attendees claimed to be a professional security expert. Some network administrators stated that they explicitly feel they are a security layperson by terms of the definition given above. If we accept the assumption that IT security is mostly maintained by non-specialists, it might be interesting to find out which skills those laypersons have, how they improve their skills and how they try to manage new IT security problems they become aware of.

The status "layperson" is obviously related to different levels of IT knowledge, from the absolute beginner up to the so-called "semi-professional". This can be done by deriving groups of laypersons with comparable skills and behaviour. Below are some examples for different layperson circles and their interactions.

1. Private PC Driver and Good Friends

The owners of private personal computers do not have much expertise in how to manage the "mainframe under the table" in a correct way. In most cases, there is no budget for software and application maintenance. This inhibits the outsourcing of security tasks to professional service providers. Good friends with higher general PC expertise are demanded to solve obvious issues and damage to software. Hidden problems remain unmanaged and security responsibilities remain unclear.

2. Ignorant "We never had problems" User

Those users often negate the existence of threats attacking their system. They believe in the overall power of the technical security implementations and interpret the absence of visible symptoms as a generalized security approval. They often misinterpret attempts to improve security awareness as commercial scareware.

3. Family's "Let's try this app too" Computer Hobbyist

Young computer experts tend to see the family's PC as a personal gaming area ready to experiment with critical software tools. Local leadership in technical knowledge may qualify them for support and consultancy questions, which may reach the new business laptop of parents too.

4. Self-Certified PC Expert

Having a long time experience with PC applications and reading IT magazines regularly, this kind of layperson adopts special knowledge in many applications and usage areas. These people are in demand for consulting and repair instance, and are often qualified by all private IT users as "the general PC expert of choice".

5. Small Business "I'm overloaded" IT Solo Dancer

In many SME (small and medium size enterprises), the IT department is a one person show. The all-in-one-IT gurus have almost no time to develop their own skills in a strategic way, as they are overloaded by routine tasks. Learning happens as short-term problem-driven learning-by-doing focussed on the main tasks to be managed. A typical behaviour is to outsource IT responsibilities by involving external expertise and time.

6. Executives

The leading edge is a major problem source. Executives often have no will to build personal IT-related skills, as they delegate every technical issue to their personal technicians. They frequently use privileged infrastructure like home offices together with critical applications like financial transaction controls. Security awareness is focused on the company's infrastructure ignoring their personal responsibility as leaders. In their perception, the IT administrator is responsible for any security issue.

C. Interference between Different Skill Levels

It is an enormous challenge to be the absolute PC expert of choice, a master of the holy IT grail in the recognition of people having much less IT experience. All the friends, colleagues, neighbours, clients and customers imply professional behaviour and knowledge, no matter how deep this expertise is on the particular IT topic in question. This attribution may cause a strong tension resulting in dangerous gaps and traps, because each of the parts has diverse needs and expectations.

As a first example, we consider the private area: From a computer newbie's viewpoint, each good friend using some PC applications regularly looks like a PC expert, no matter how deep the expertise is. If this friend is of the category "self-certified", it is impossible for the beginner to verify the level of professionalism in a special area without the help of a third-party's opinion. In terms of IT security, the "leading layperson" is responsible to inform the "following layperson" about their limitations in expertise and has to discuss the need for a third-party.

From a parent's viewpoint, children learn media usage like breathing. Very often, the kids possess a healthy margin in technical knowledge, which makes it nearly impossible for parents to keep parental control software on the family PC operational for long. On the other hand, the contribution of some adult guidance is very important, as the juvenile tech experts are laypersons in terms of media competence and risk management. Again, the interaction of both laity groups may benefit from a clear understanding of each other's responsibilities and the integration of third-party support. The role of the "leading layperson" should be taken by the experienced adult person having significantly less technical skills; however it might be a good idea to delegate the management of all technical tasks to the "following person".

In the next chapter, another important information security laity circle and its role interference is discussed: The interaction between IT staff and executives.

II. Executive's Responsibility for IT Security

In his book "The art of digital defense" Thomas Werth recommends: "A corporate security guideline has to start with the written regulation, that the top management is responsible for the IT security in total and has to commit to all objectives, concepts and procedures described in the security guidelines. This general responsibility remains on top. If tasks derived from the guidelines are delegated from the executive to staff members or corporate divisions, … the top management has to invoke the security guidelines and has to enforce them as an obligatory standard to be fulfilled by each employee" (Werth, 2009:86 f.)

A TOP approach to corporate information security defines three pillars to be built and maintained in order to generate a sufficient overall protection level. The TOP acronym describes the pillars Technical instrumentation, Organisational standards of security-keeping processes and Personnel development of activities dedicated to improve security awareness.

Having all three pillars in mind, a responsible authority has to perform a balanced risk management guided by the principle of the weakest link of a chain.

A. Responsibility Gaps in SME

Large organizations and enterprises usually apply this strategy. The top management incorporates a CIO, who implements an enterprise-wide concept within the organizational pyramid by providing each staff member with appropriate IT-security-relevant rules, tasks and responsibilities.

This is not the case in small and medium size enterprises (SME), where the executive typically locates the primary responsibility for information security at the head of the IT department (Jörg, 2008: 10), because security is mainly considered as a matter of technology. But this is critical misunderstanding of the situation.

The IT admin is not able to serve such "all-inclusive" responsibility demands:

- He is not responsible for organizational standards beyond IT processes
- He is not responsible for human resources and personnel development
- He can't self-control nor self-audit his technical security provisioning
- The executives are not permitted to delegate their legal liability

Unlike the situation in large IT departments, there is no chance for the head of a small IT group to delegate the daily IT workload and to join the board. The security gap is widening tremendously if the IT structure is performing similar to the one-man show described above. Saturated with keeping the digital heartbeat of the company running, no IT staff member has the time to update non-urgently needed skills and therefore act as a layperson. In addition, the usual pressure valve "outsourcing" may lead to a situation, where the executive forwards responsibility to the company's IT department, while the head of IT forwards it to external services.

Service providers will always locate the main responsibility at the customer's top management, as they are able to deliver technical services only. If there is no written guideline with a clear definition of the particular responsibilities of all stakeholders, a dangerous vicious circle may arise, where many weak links in the chain remain unidentified.

B. Skill Development in the IT department

In the last century, the German IT vocational training outside universities was aimed at four different job titles, each profession covering a broad spectrum of IT-related tasks. After some years of practise, the IT staff started to specialize leaving broad parts of their vocational training undeveloped. In 2003, the German Federal Ministry of Education and Research started an investigation focusing on typical processes in the daily work of IT professionals.

The result was a bunch of very different workload profiles, leading to the definition of 29 new IT specialist professions. Those different professional profiles are grouped into categories (administrators, solution developers, software developers, coordinators, advisers and technicians) characterising the general type of workload.

Only one of those different profiles, the "IT security coordinator" covers all the essential tasks to be performed in today's professional information security. The reference task list of this profile contains more tasks related to communication with non-technical staff than most other profiles. Nevertheless this profile is not categorized in the group "coordinators", who concentrate on communication tasks, but part of the "solution developers", the group characterizing wide-spread holistic workload profiles. Some of the reference tasks of the "IT Security Coordinator" profile are reaching the executive level, e.g. "external representation of the company as a whole in all matters of security" (Rogalla et al., 2004: 95 ff.).

This outcome of the German government's investigation of IT skill building requirements shows that the specialist's profile "IT security coordinator" is rather a generalist's profile. This implies an increasing challenge for skill updating, as outlined in the introduction.

C. IT Security Knowledge Updating in SME

In his thesis, Christian Jörg describes as a result of his analysis of information security in German SMEs, that the IT staff there have to be classified as security laypersons in terms of their knowledge management. He summarizes: „The lack of certified security qualifications obstruct the improvement of information security in the SMEs of all business sectors".

In particular, the results show that "the amount of certified security-relevant add-on qualifications gained by employees who are responsible for information security is averaging nearly zero … Staff in charge of security show a strong tendency for very sporadic professional development activities with an annual average of less than two days spent for courses related to security topics" (Jörg, 2008: 195).

III. The Constant Grow of the Human Risk Factor

For over 40 years, the nature of information security has regularly changed. David Lacey describes the history in terms of human security awareness:

"In 1970 the concept of risk assessment was introduced. The focus of attention for security controls was limited to individual systems and machines. ... Since 1990, the focus of security moved towards the enterprise infrastructure. ... The early years of the 21st century introduced a much stronger external perspective. Networks stretched beyond enterprise boundaries to embrace the public Internet. But the primary focus of most security managers remained largely on security needs within the enterprise ...

We also need to start paying attention to the extramural security behaviour of users. Working from home, portfolio careers and social networking are removing the traditional barrier between business and personal lifestyles. This trend is irreversible ... The challenge is to understand, accept and manage the consequential security risks of a business environment, that's now everywhere but nowhere in particular. It's no less than a major paradigm shift for business and security." (Lacey, 2009:15ff)

In 2007, Bruce Schneier discussed the situation of home users as "A Public Health Problem?" (Schneier, 2008:243f). He demanded professional support and proposed a new type of information security to be provisioned and managed by Internet service providers connecting the home user's network. In the same year, he broached the issue of the risk coming up from the increased usage of insecure computer disks and portable drives. (Schneier, 2008:230ff)

Let's have a closer look at such an attack vector with low technical effort, which can't be defended at workplaces by technical barriers alone, no matter how much is invested. It illustrates the urgent demand for organizational and personnel defense activities, as human behaviour and habit is the weakest link of the chain.

A. Conficker's USB Attack

Mobile data storage with USB connectors are very wide spread and comfortable, as the USB interface allows hot plugging into running systems, acceptable transfer rates and inbound power supply, if the storage is based on cheap flash memory. It appears as conventional USB-"stick" format, but also as digital camera's storage.

The big trend towards mobile computing forced the development of portable apps, which can start from the plugged-in storage automatically and offer data processing service without program installation. The big market for digital consumer cameras let many private photographers become familiar with a device-oriented workflow, where the connection of a camera opens an "autoplay" menu.

This offers all image processing tools installed on the PC like picture viewers, direct printing of pictures, quality enhancement tools and other useful data handling options. The operating system builds the menu dynamically according to the content formats found on the storage device. It also allows menu items to be added to start portable software. This “autoplay” menu is offered to the user, who has to decide which particular processing option has to be started. This is very comfortable, but very dangerous as well:

The automated start-up of portable code by background services is the key behaviour of viral malware, the basic process, which turns a harmless data file into malicious action. A simple four lines text file can attack your system, if it’s name is “autorun.inf” and it’s place is the main directory of the USB-hotplug device.

B. Beginner’s 1st Malicious Coding Exercise

The first example shows the start of an external program triggered from digital camera’s USB storage. The autoplay menu invites the user to choose the external program as the best of options presented.

```
1 [Autorun]
2 ShellExecute="%SystemRoot%\system32\calc.exe"
3 Action=Open Folder
4 Icon=%systemroot%\system32\shell32.dll,-5
```

Figure 1: Plain Text File “Autorun.inf” - basic exploit

This file on the portable device adds a new menu item to the bunch of options offered by the autoplay function. The new menu item “Open Folder” (named by line 3) looks like the original one, as it uses the original icon of the operating system (pulled from Windows resources by line 4). As a wide door opener, the added menu item is marked by default. Pressing the ‘Enter’ key is enough to run it.

Unlike the original Windows function, the faked menu item does not open the folder of the USB-stick, but runs the program defined by line 2. In this example, the calculator of the PC is started. There is no software needed on the USB-stick except this plain text file autorun.inf.

As the “Open Folder” option is now available twice in the menu, a careful observing user may recognize the attack condition easily. Unfortunately, the default Windows options “Open Folder” and “No Action” stay on the very bottom position of the menu, while Windows adds the new dynamic menu item on the top. If the menu list is longer than the fixed size of the window, the harmful duplication of an entry is detectable only by scrolling. In case of digital cameras, there are typically some picture files on the storage, which force Windows to fill the autoplay menu up with all the picture processing options available on the PC. In fact, the existence of harmless picture files somewhere in the flash memory helps increasing the impact of the attack, as it increases the amount of menu items. This helps fooling the user by obfuscation of the twin appearance of a function.

```
[Autorun]
ShellExecute=.\Recycler\S-5-3-418.jpg          .exe
Action=No Action
Icon=%systemroot%\system32\shell32.dll,-338
```

Figure 2: Plain text file "Autorun.inf" - offensive exploit

Figure 2 shows an USB attack aiming to fool the paranoid user, who always presses the "No Action" button. Line 4 pulls the appropriate "prohibition sign" icon out of the Windows repository. In line 2, a malicious program is executed, which is placed in the camera's recycle bin and appears as a picture file, while the .exe file type appendix is obfuscated by a long number of blanks.

USB sticks equipped with such a simple attack are very difficult to prevent by guarding and hardening software, as most computer users have acquired a habit to use the sticks - in their private area at least. As this infection worked in both directions, it is able to hook on the stick from a home PC. This is one of the penetrators the worm Conficker used successfully to spread into many networks. After penetration, the worm builds a bridgehead on the infected system, which tries to download the Conficker´s complex malicious payload from the public network.

C. Technical Defense Performance

As Conficker was surprisingly successful even in very big networks, it should be discussed first, why technical guards and hardening procedures failed.

1. Firewalls

Firewalls are not able to defend the "USB" pathway, because the user himself is the transport layer and interface. Firewalls are designed to prevent inbound program access from the uncontrolled public network. Most of the outbound data flow is passing that barrier in order to enable regular working tasks. The firewall's only chance to intercept the attack is the moment where the bridgehead loader tries to get the malicious payload from the public network. Software firewalls running on the infected machine can easily be fooled by the bridgehead code, while external hardware firewalls would require a central inspection of the complete outbound data flow for suspicious packets by pattern analysis.

2. Malware Scanner

Traditional malware scanners are signature-based and need permanent update processing to compete with the changing appearance of malware. The threatening situation is turning more and more dangerous, as signature-based scanning needs increasing processing power while false-positive alarms increase tremendously. Modern penetrators are designed by construction kits producing unique instances of code pattern, while the bridgehead part is equipped to fool both software firewall and malware scanner in charge long before the relevant signature update may arrive. Beside the core job to classify file patterns, today's virus scanners turn more and more into intrusion detection systems analyzing rootkits, detecting web browser exploits, observing patch level management and testing the behaviour of suspicious programs prior to execution. As those add-on jobs eat up huge parts of the total processor power, they are often switched off in enterprise environments.

3. Patch Level Management

The necessity for a permanent update of critical software parts is well known, but not easy to perform. Central software parts like the operating system and web browsers may handle this automatically, but it is turning to be a fulltime job to maintain patch levels and interdependencies of all parts showing critical vulnerabilities. Consequently, the attack vectors turn during the last months towards the application level of browser plugins, namely Flash, Quicktime and Acrobat Reader.

Each vendor of exposed products has his own way to weigh the severity of a security hole that has come into focus. Up to March 2009, a fully patched Windows XP did execute all USB autoplay files automatically without presenting a menu first. Staying up-to-date with all security alerts would require the careful administrator to block essential parts of the user's workplace as long as a patch is not available. Many administrators decide to ignore this, because temporal blocking reduces the availability of business processes and increase the administrator's workload.

4. Administrative Rights Management

One of the most effective technical barriers against malware is working without administrative rights. "Don't do risky things as long as you have a demolition license" is the mantra all laymen have to incorporate. This might be hard to explain at an executive level, as executives in their main business profile need to have full administrative rights in order to perform their administrative duties efficiently.

5. Effective Protection against the USB attack

The bottom line is that the only 100% secure technical defense tactic against the USB attack is the sealing off of all free USB connectors on each computer. If this is not possible, because unoccupied USB outlets are needed in the workflow, an effective USB protection requires the implementation of a TOP approach.

D. TOPerational Consequences

For the whole organisation, a stringent policy has to be developed on how USB devices must be handled. All users have to be instructed about that rule set, especially each new member of the staff. The probably most challenging part of this TOP protection is the enforcement of the policy as an obligatory requirement for each employee to become and stay part of the organisation.

IV. Challenges of Today and Tomorrow

A. Responsibility Management

It is obvious, that this kind of approach is not applicable for delegation from the executive manager to a technical department or to an external technology and IT service provider. Top-level managers can't disown their responsibility to integrate technology and human development into an organisational structure reflecting the business processes to be performed by the corporation.

B. External Auditing and Certification

External services may provide security auditing and certification processes that help to understand the challenges of change management. This includes a clear definition and assignment of responsibilities to different internal departments and external support roles. The key questions are: Who is in charge of the IT documentation? Who is responsible for the IT training and corporate skill development?

Personal job profile certificates like the German "IT Security Coordinator" may solve the HR manager's problem of how to approve the qualification of a candidate in detail to get a correct set of skills. Personal certificates according to DIN/ISO/EN/IEC 17024 provide a policy for European-wide comparable procedures on how to monitor the competence of individuals. This rule set certifies that the candidates have performed all key processes of a job profile by themselves. This is fundamentally different from the usual knowledge-testing examination, which can't evaluate any practical abilities. (*Grunwald et al.*, 2005:29 f.)

C. Near Workplace Learning and Support

The world of interacting and networking stakeholders offers a chance for each organisation willing to develop itself to become a learning organisation. The increased usage of social networks and personal career building on the base of individual skill portfolios enables the organisation to master tomorrow's threatening positions. Future key challenges in this security improvement process will be:

How to support security layperson's skill building at the workplace?

How to manage contemporary security skills sustainably TOP down?

References:

- GRUNWALD, S., T. FREITAG, D. WITT-SCHLEUER. 2005. *Zertifizierung im IT-Weiterbildungssystem: Das Prüfungshandbuch*. Hannover: Heise
- JÖRG, C. 2008. *Informationssicherheit in deutschen klein- und mittelständischen Unternehmen: eine empirische Analyse von Implementationsbarrieren*. Hamburg: Kovač
- LACEY, D. 2009. *Managing the Human Factor in Information Security: How to win over staff and influence business managers*. New York, NY : Wiley, J
- ROGALLA, I., D. WITT-SCHLEUER. 2004. *IT-Weiterbildung mit System: Das Praxishandbuch*. Hannover: Heise
- SCHNEIER, B. 2008. *Schneier on Security*. New York, NY : Wiley, J
- WERTH, T. 2009. *Die Kunst der digitalen Verteidigung*. Böblingen : C & L.

Aleš Završnik

Criminal Justice Systems' (Over)Reactions to IT Security Threats

Responses by criminal justice systems to cybersecurity threats show how the solutions of problems can become problems on their own. The harm caused by cybersecurity incidents may well be exceeded by the harm caused by the criminal justice system's response to the incidents, especially considering that the criminal justice system is the most powerful (coercive) system of formal control. The central thesis is that some criminal law solutions and responses by criminal justice systems to cybersecurity threats across Europe and the USA raise substantial public policy and human rights concerns. The thesis is explained by presenting the scale of the cybercrime "problem" on one hand and the reaction to the "problem" on the other hand. The paper shows how the assessment of dangerousness of cybercrime varies considerably between different stakeholders such as the Council of Europe, private companies and the International Telecommunications Union. The criminal justice systems reaction to the problem, on the other hand, is analysed in the light of data retention regulation and other cybercrime prevention strategies, cybercrime policing, substantive criminal law solutions (for instance criminalisation of virtual child pornography and illegal access) and challenges of criminal procedure (for instance on-line searches and seizures). The reaction to cybercrime forms a part of a larger cultural trend and shifts in crime policy heading towards an increased criminalisation of on-line activities and intense cyber-surveillance. The paper shows how the open and (relatively) free nature of the internet can be destroyed by the very "fight" against "cybersecurity threats".

I. Introduction

Current responses by criminal justice systems to cybersecurity threats show how the solutions of problems can become problems on their own and how not only cybersecurity threats and incidents cause damage and problems but also the reaction to these problems by a criminal justice system that is the most powerful and coercive system of formal control.[1]

The article focuses on cybercrime as it is perceived and responded to by criminal justice systems in some European nation states and the USA. The perception and

[1] For the purpose of the article, the notion of a "criminal justice system" is used in a broad sense. It encompasses not only the activities of public agencies, the police, prosecutors and criminal courts, but also the legislation guiding these actors, i.e. criminal codes, criminal procedures, ("preventive") data retention regulation etc. For instance, in comparison to the analysis of cybersecurity networks made by Nhan and Huey (2008), which identified four "nodal clusters" or "sets of institutional actors", the broad notion of the "criminal justice system" encompasses not only the law enforcement "nodal cluster" but also the government's activities.

response is "measured" by analysis of selected national criminal legislation and solutions contained in international legal documents. The article's central thesis is that criminal law solutions and the response of criminal justice systems have raised substantial public policy and human rights concerns.[2] The once central dilemma in the theory of cybercrime between "old wine new bottles" protagonists (*Grabosky*, 2001) and "new wine no bottles" protagonists (*Wall*, 2007) has evolved into a dilemma of how to stop the dark future of the Internet, i.e. "dark" from the human rights perspective. By looking closely at the cumbersome responses of criminal justice agencies to cybercrime, the paper starts from the thesis advocated by Zittrain (2008) that today we must face up to real problems that are occurring in cyberspace. These problems deserve to be scrutinised in detail and cannot be disregarded as mere nuisances. Failure to confront problems like spam or the underground botnet industry can lead to a shadowy future for the Internet. However, the current eager "fight" against "cybersecurity threats" that we are witnessing in the most technologically advanced societies, I suggest, will also destroy the open nature of the Internet, since the "fight" has a serious impact on civil liberties. At least some of the legal solutions either incorporated in national criminal codes or in supranational regulation and shifts in the organisational-managerial domain of criminal justice agencies that reflect the cultural impact of IT are firmly heading towards an over-regulated Internet. We are witnessing a situation in which on-line activities are becoming more regulated than their off-line counterparts.

On a general level, the article will show how the reaction to cybercrime and "cybersecurity threats" – a notion that is particularly indiscriminately used for all sorts of threats, nuisances and accidents – form a part of the microcosm of larger cultural trends, processes and shifts in criminal justice policy throughout occidental societies. In particular, a part of the wider cultural shift toward a punitive crime policy, increased criminalisation of everyday life and intense cyber-surveillance.

Before entering into the question of the adequacy of criminal justice system measures in the light of fundamental civil liberties, it is essential to assess the harm of cybercrime. Although the harm of cybercrime is to some extent not completely discernible, it will be compared with the effects of the criminal justice system's "fight" against cybercrime. The central question that will be tackled is: what threatens us more, the problem (i.e. cybercrime) or the reaction to the problem (i.e., the intervention of criminal justice systems)?

---

[2] In adopting IT into its operation, the criminal justice system itself becomes a potential target of, for instance, computer integrity offences and computer related (or assisted) crimes. Those acts can be performed against judicial case management systems, video conferencing systems (such as prison video links, remote witness systems) etc. This, although an interesting theme, is not the focus of the article.

II. The scale of the cybercrime "problem"

A. "Be afraid" arguments

The history of the Council of Europe's (CoE hereinafter) engagement in the "fight" against cybercrime illustrates the challenges associated with the perception and evaluation of the scope of cybercrime threats. According to the Council of Europe's report from the *Octopus Interface 2007 Conference* (*Council of Europe*, 2007) trends in cyber security are far from encouraging. It was claimed that:

(1) Information societies worldwide are increasingly dependent on information and communication technologies and the growth of cybercrimes renders societies highly vulnerable;

(2) Malware (malicious codes and software, spyware, bots and botnets) is evolving and spreading rapidly, and is being used, among other things, to commit 'denial of service attacks', identity thefts, frauds, money laundering;

(3) Spam represents the vast majority of email traffic and is not only a nuisance but is increasingly a carrier of malware: in addition, spam messages are also appearing in new technologies (on mobile phones as SMSishing or internet phones as Vishing);

(4) Botnets are one of the central tools of organised cyber crime used for DoS attacks, identity thefts, phishing, as well as for the placing of adware and spyware;

(5) An underground service economy is developing (botnets are being leased to organised criminal groups);

(6) The internet is misused for the sexual exploitation and abuse of children and human trafficking;

(8) The risk of cyber-attacks against critical information infrastructure (cyber-terrorism and cyber-war) is on the increase;

(9) The use of P-2-P networks enables widespread copyright infringements;

(10) The material damage caused by cybercrime is put at a cost at around 50 billion dollars a year.

If we accept this report in its entirety, the only possible conclusion is that cybercrime clearly and seriously threatens our information societies. However, the next CoE's *Octopus Interface 2008 Conference* (*Council of Europe*, 2008a) was more balanced in terms of stressing the seriousness of threats posed by cybercrimc. The report (*Council of Europe*, 2008b) notes that countries all over the world are strengthening their legislation, using the Convention on Cybercrime as a guideline, and that the mobilisation of states' involvement in the "fight" against cybercrime had been successful. The report explicitly indicates the fundamental rights that "have to be respected in the fight against cybercrime". The previously eager "fight" against cybercrime that had drawn the critical attention of NGOs and the academic community is thus balanced by recognition of the need to respect fundamental liberties. Their concerns are at least formally declared, if not yet fully put into practice. The focus of the conference had shifted from raising awareness in order to persuade states to shift priorities and resources into a search for a new paradigm of "Internet governance" that would welcome other stakeholders into cybercrime policing. The "fight" against cybercrime has thus evolved. At that point in time, it was entrusted to an emerging "public-private partnership", i.e. to an assemblage of industry with the dominant role of internet service providers (ISPs) and law enforcement agencies.

The invitation to the CoE's most recent *Octopus Interface 2009 Conference* (*Council of Europe*, 2009) does not mention the harm of cybercrime to "information societies". The last conference was dedicated to fostering cooperation between law enforcement agencies and internet service providers, to a goal especially high on the political agenda after the postponed application of the EU Data Retention Directive's provisions on retention of data related to internet access, e-mail and internet telephony (VoiP).[3] The shift in cybercrime policy is now firmly focusing on private security models. Private entities are perceived as the only ones capable of providing efficient cybercrime countermeasures and are encouraged to enter into public-private partnerships.

The CoE's ambitions in the fight against cybercrime represent a good example of raising fear of cybercrime. Nevertheless, the CoE's reports are actually among the most balanced views on cybercrime and crime control. Private software companies' reports are substantially more frightening. Symantec, for instance, in reports entitled "Cybercrime Continues to Rise" (2006) and "Report on the Underground Economy" (2008) suggests that there is a Mafia type of underground economy beyond the reach of law. Its reports associate cybercrime with the imagery of the "wild-wild East" and "Cyber-Balkans", i.e., the imagery of Russian and eastern European neo-liberal societies in which criminals are at the centre of drugs, SUVs and prostitutes.

In addition to private companies' profit-motivated reports on cybercrime, which, instead of unfolding the problem, reveal their own motivation in tackling the problem, non-profit organisations' reports can also sometimes be problematic. They are often trapped in their own institutional dynamics and concerned with pursuing their own agenda. For instance, the Information Telecommunications Union's (ITU hereinafter) reports and recommendations are often difficult to assess and evaluate. Until the development of the internet, the ITU had been at the centre of worldwide communications regulation. However, due to its decentred architecture, the internet has radically modified the structure of decision-making in telecommunications.

---

[3] The Directive 2006/24/EC of the European Parliament and of the Council of 15 March 2006 on the retention of data generated or processed in connection with the provision of publicly available electronic communications services or of public communications networks and amending Directive 2002/58/EC (The Data Retention Directive hereinafter).

Governance of the decentralised networks differs substantially from its predecessor – the telephone system. The ITU is thus trying to keep pace with the development of internet governance models. It is based on the post-WW2 distribution of power among nation states, with their power culminating in the UN. Governance of the internet core infrastructure, though, in contrast, is very decentralized and lead by multiple entities. As the oldest UN agency, with its origins back in the 19th century, the ITU has been very successful in pursuing its own agenda. It clearly thus has its own institutionally embedded interests in the type of evolution of the "fight" against cybercrime. It is inclined to support nation states in furthering their own interests and views on cyberspace as part of their national territory.[4] The ITU's engagement in the cybersecurity agenda is, therefore, clearer if we consider its diminishing power in worldwide regulation of the Internet and its determination to play a more profound role through the augmented importance of nation states in the internet governance model.

The following chapter focuses on the other side of the "cybercrime problem" spectrum: why should we be afraid of cybercrime? What does the notion of cybersecurity denote? What are the mostly quoted reports that anticipate the Zero day of the internet actually implying?

B. The "but why the fear?" arguments

The very concept of cybercrime is still very vague. There are different types of "lenses" used to observe cybercrime and, consequently, many contradictory "facts" about its scope, as well as a variety of assessments of the dangers it poses. The vast literature about the nature of cybercrime can be divided into a number of discourses. *Wall* (2007: 12 ff.), for instance, identifies (1) the legislative discourse about cybercrime, which attempts to define the rules that set boundaries for (un)acceptable behaviour, (2) the academic discourse, which seeks to understand the phenomenon through computer science, information management, economics, the socio-legal and criminological disciplines, (3) expert knowledge, which explores and seeks to understand trends in cybercrimes in order to provide explanations and inform solutions and (4) the popular/layperson's discourse, which reflects a "common sense-based" understanding of crime.

The problem we face today is that all these different discourses, approaches or narratives are incoherent, and their claims to knowledge contradictory. Do acts labelled "cybercrimes" really represent a "clear and present danger" to our "information societies" which in turn requires the machinery of the criminal justice system to be set in motion?

---

[4] The US and China are very similar in their perception of a borderless Internet. Gagnon (2008) has shown that they both perceive the Internet as a "place" in which they can impose their sovereignty.

The trends listed in the CoE Octopus Interface Conference Reports and the diverse phenomenology (of definitions and taxonomies) of cybercrime show, firstly, that the identification and analysis of cyber threats is still an arduous task. Some forms of cybercrime "only" use computers and networks as a means for committing conventional crime, while others focus primarily on computers, networks and data; some are computer crimes (the so-called first generation of cybercrime), others involve hacking (second generation) and some automated forms of cybercrime (third generation) (*Wall*, 2007: 130 ff.).

Secondly, the list of trends shows that the assessment of the danger of cybercrime is self-contradictory. According to the above mentioned CoE reports, and the CoE is undoubtedly one of the most important forums for the protection of human rights, we should be afraid of the threat that the problems in this list pose to individuals; actually, very afraid. Not only that the trends are scary by themselves, also the trend that there must be a network of technological players, legal players and moral entrepreneurs to keep the place secure gives another spin to the anxiety of cyber threats.

However, many criminologists advise us not to draw such conclusions (*Levi*, 2001; *Wall*, 2002; *Wall*, 2007). They claim that this anxiety is being provoked, quite intentionally, by certain parties pursuing their economic interests and by others trying to make their voice heard in the process of reallocating public funds. For instance, the case of spam clearly shows us how the dangers of cybercrime can be exaggerated. At the beginning of 2007, there were estimates that spam represented 80 percent of e-mail traffic in 2005, 95 percent in 2006 and that the system would reach its capacity in 2007 (See *Rowan*, 2006; *Cheng*, 2007; *Barracuda Networks*, 2007). This disaster has (thankfully) not occurred, but "anxiety-provokers" will quickly add that has been averted only due to the system's ability to adapt; should this fail, we shall be in trouble. Perhaps the pessimists' claim has some weight, but the performance data supplied by sources in criminal justice systems across Europe (i.e., statistics from police forces, prosecution services and criminal courts) provide controversial evidence that the numbers of reported crimes, as well as prosecuted and processed cases, are simply not increasing as quickly as some claim and fear; moreover, that they do not justify a verdict as dire as that which the CoE's reports would have us reach. On the contrary, the numbers themselves are extremely low and contrast sharply with the non-numerical "situation analysis" the reports offer.

The criminal justice system's relation to IT is twofold. As a mechanism of formal crime control, it reacts to threats posed by crime strengthened by the new technology (the approach encompassed in the notion of the "fight" against cybercrime). On the other hand, criminal justice systems simultaneously integrate and adopt IT solutions in order to be more efficient (for instance, to gather, store and analyse information about criminals and crimes). The next chapter examines the reaction in both crime policy perspectives, i.e. the preventive and the repressive perspective. The former includes "soft" shifts in crime policy. Prevention strategies mirror organisational shifts of criminal justice agencies and cultural representations of the seriousness of cybercrime. The repressive perspective encompasses "hard" criminal law reactions to cybercrime. These reactions are manifested in re-interpretations and reinventions of substantive criminal law and criminal procedure.

III. IT and the criminal justice system complex

IT has generated new forms of harm and provoked a new criminal justice response to this harm labelled as crime. (1) Substantive criminal law challenges have raised a dilemma between "old wine new bottles" and "new wine no bottles" approaches in criminological theory. Today, it seems that the dilemma is a rather academic one, since the boundary between the old rules (re)interpreted in a new way ("old wine new bottles") and completely new rules ("new wine no bottles") depends on the definition of law. What actually are we looking at: law in action or law in books? Either way, new concepts such as *information*, *computers* and *networks* (*Walden*, 2007) have raised the latter approach to the fore of criminological and criminal law inquiry. Taxonomies of cybercrimes are numerous today, but at least criminal law theorists mainly refer to the most notorious and (legislatively) influential substantive criminal law taxonomy from the CoE Convention on Cybercrime (CoE Convention hereinafter).[5] Because technological development brings to the fore new IT products on a daily basis, it is impossible to make once-and-for-all definitions of cybercrime. New types of connections, devices and services will surely keep substantial criminal law challenges on the research agenda in the years to come.

On the other hand, criminal justice systems have responded to new types of crime not only by adapting substantial criminal law provisions and introducing new crimes. Today, it seems that moulding new taxonomies and definitions of cybercrime was only the first part of a wider process of "criminal justice complex" engagement in cyberspace. Faced with the need for efficient crime control, the agents of the criminal justice system have also changed their mode of conduct, thus also (2) new rules of criminal procedure and (3) new technologically enhanced crime prevention strategies have been introduced. Although changes to substantial provisions of criminal law have caused manifold challenges, I suggest that these modifications have not (yet) fundamentally changed the very nature of the "criminal justice complex". As we shall see, the combination of risk management mentalities has led to enhanced pre-crime activities of state actors. Furthermore, crime control has become "big business" and pre-crime control is not only performed by state actors, but also by public-private partnership entities, state's surrogates and sometimes its competitors. Changes in crime prevention strategies illuminate not only evolutionary re-wiring of the "criminal justice complex" mechanisms, but fundamentally revolutionary changes of legal adjudication.

---

[5] See a critique of the taxonomy in McGuire, 2007.

A. Cybercrime prevention strategies

Although new technologically enhanced crime prevention strategies are manifold, there is a specific measure that lies at the core of the "data nation" regulatory framework. It is obligatory retention of traffic data, location data, subscriber data and facts/circumstances with regard to unsuccessful call attempts (hereinafter traffic data) related to internet access, e-mail and internet telephony. The regulation was introduced with the post 9/11 Patriot Act[6] in the USA and the Data Retention Directive in the EU. According to *Bloss* (2007) the Patriot Act modified or revised fifteen federal laws, focusing primarily on counter-terrorism and foreign intelligence, and became the catalyst for statutory surveillance revisions. The EU Data Retention Directive has had similar surveillance effects. Some states and numerous non-state stakeholders have protested against the directive,[7] Ireland and Poland most decisively by disputing it before the European Court of Justice (ECJ). At least for now (i.e., August 2009), we are stuck with the directive, since the ECJ has only decided that the directive was correctly adopted on the basis of the EC Treaty, since it relates predominantly to the functioning of the internal market.[8] This may change, since the ECJ will have to take a stand on the issue of whether or not the directive violates the right to privacy (Charter of Fundamental Rights). Although privacy rights advocates have strong reasons to be optimistic about ECJ adjudication,[9] viewed realistically, the court has so far always followed the *Avocat General*'s opinion explained the directive as a proportionate measure to fight "serious crime".

The impact of IT on crime control cannot be appropriately evaluated without recognizing the trend of amplified usage of IT in policing. "Intelligence-led policing" (*Lemieux*, 2008) is becoming the prototype of all police work. Data gathering, its storage,[10] analysis ("data mining" techniques) and transmission of digitised data, the introduction of expert analysts and their high-tech tools in the crime investigation process has caused a revolution in policing (*Lemieux*, 2008). According to *Bloss* (2007: 211), advances in technology have substantially contributed to the ability of

---

6 "Uniting and Strengthening America by Providing Appropriate Tools Required to Intercept and Obstruct Terrorism Act", later known as the "USA Patriot Act of 2001" (hereafter Patriot Act).

7 For instance, in Italy "The Electronic Frontiers Italy" (ALCEI), in Romania "Asociatia pentru Tehnologie si Internet" (A.P.T.I.), in UK "The Privacy International" (PI), in Macedonia the NGO alliance "Metamorphosis", in Germany "The German Working Group on Data Retention" (AK Vorrat) and in Bulgaria "Access to Information Program (AIP) Foundation". See European Digital Rights, 2009.

8 See the Judgment of the Court of Justice of the European Communities in case Ireland v. Parliament and Council (Case C-301/06).

9 For instance, the German Working Group on Data Retention, which coordinated 34,000 plaintiffs applying to the German Constitutional Court to seek a separate ruling on the compatibility of data retention with human rights. See The German Working Group on Data Retention, 2009.

10 The scope of data storage is leading us to a "data nation" society. See Garfinkel, 2000.

the police to engage in electronic surveillance of citizens, since personal electronic communications can be intercepted with greater ease and, to some extent, with less physical intrusion. What we are witnessing today is a transformation of policing, the introduction of new operational approaches and surveillance practices that focus more on information and intelligence gathering (*Peterson*, 2005; *Carter*, 2004).

The IT triggered paradigm shift is further enhanced by the widening police surveillance capabilities that are a result of collaboration with private commercial enterprises. Private entities can obtain personal data and eavesdrop on the public more than ever before (*O'Harrow*, 2005; *Bridis and Solomon*, 2006). The reasons for such "joint ventures" in policing endeavours, according to Bloss (2007), are a result of a failure. They are a countermeasure to the police's lack of manpower and technical expertise. The cumulative outcome of the IT effect on criminal justice system is thus very controversial. There is a reluctance on the part of legal professionals working in the system to use IT, on the one hand, but there is also a very strong effect of IT in what *Cole* (2007) refers to as "preventive law enforcement". That is a tendency to use greater surveillance powers to reduce threats and prosecute offenders (*Nhan and Huey*, 2008). Similarly, according to *Leman-Langlois* (2008: 6), more than ever before and in any other type of late-modern policing, "technopolicing" involves multiple entities. State-centred police organizations are but one actor in the overall production of "technosecurity". Furthermore, in a different terminology put forward by *Nhan* and *Huey* (2008), there are now different types of "nodal clusters" or "sets of institutional actors" that must be taken into account when elaborating contemporary policing: in addition to government and law enforcement, also private industry and the general public.

The paradigm of cybercrime policing has initiated institutional rearrangements of order-maintenance. *Wall* (2007), for instance, identifies an assemblage of actors engaged in cyber policing that are forming a "multi-layer order-maintenance assemblage". This order-maintenance complex encompasses new police and prosecution forces and new e-justice concepts (embodied, for instance, in video-conferencing and computer animation), but not limited to only these traditional actors that were once central in maintaining order. When identifying the "multi-agency cross-sector partnerships", *Wall* (2007) specifies a range of new actors, such as internet users' organisations, virtual environment managers, network infrastructure providers, private corporate security personnel, non-governmental non-police hybrids (such as CERTs) and governmental non-police bodies (such as customs), which are all focused on security maintenance alongside the public (governmental) police.

The next section will narrow the examination of the IT impact on the criminal justice system to cybercrime and examine substantive criminal law and criminal procedure provisions. It must be said that cybercrime should be taken seriously and something has to be done in order to stop spam and remove the threat that botnets pose to critical information infrastructure. The creators of the internet in its early stage derived from a different ethics. The "gift culture" milieu of the early networks, with the non-proprietary ends of its early users, is interwoven into the internet. However, subsequent commercialisation of the internet has enlarged the possibilities of malevolent use(r)s of the networks. Nevertheless, the threats have to be dealt with a "trembling hand". In so doing, one has to take two additional facts into account. On the one hand, there is a tendency in the literature on cybercrime to use vague anxiety provoking terms such as "cybersecurity", which do not carry much (or any?) explanatory power.[11] On the other hand, there is an increasing desire to control cyberspace (*Gagnon*, 2008) and we should pay attention to the illusion that when we are told (that) there is such thing as "computer crime", the concepts seems closer to the natural laws that gave us computers than to the artificial laws that gave us crimes. In reality, according to *Leman-Langlois* (2008: 4), "technocrime is a Gordian knot of political interests, economic interests, legal rules, technological developments, police, private security and forensics expertise ... and other forms of power we have yet to map."

B. Substantive criminal law challenges

1. Content crime

The categories of content-related cybercrime that are particularly controversial in terms of fundamental rights and liberties, especially the right to privacy and freedom of expression, are criminalization of virtual child pornography and criminalization of extreme and violent pornography.

The UN Convention on the Rights of the Child defines a "child" as a "human being younger than 18 years" (Article 1). Both the CoE's Convention and the EU Council Framework Decision on combating the sexual exploitation of children and child pornography[12] (hereinafter EU Framework Decision on child pornography) define a child in the same way. It is doubtful whether the age limit is appropriate for all countries, since juvenile offenders are not exempted from criminal responsibility in some countries. A situation in which they can be held fully criminally responsible for their acts but are simultaneously exempted from being able to decide about their sexual representation is at least unbalanced. The CoE Convention thus enables states to set a lower age limit, but there is no equivalent reservation in the EU Framework Decision on child pornography.

---

[11] *Doria* (2007) explains that "cybersecurity" is understood differently by "techies" and lawyers, criminologists and national security experts. It is unclear whether it denotes technical, criminological, sociological or legal aspects of security. It is also unclear what is the object of such security: network safety, computer safety, safety of society, of e-business, fundamental liberties or national sovereignty?

[12] 2004/68/JHA of 22 December 2003.

There are many types of child pornography. Real child pornography should be distinguished from images of children in provocative presentations (for instance "child glamour presentations", "non-nude child sites") and from virtual child pornography. The creation of child pornography is very likely to have been connected with child abuse (New York v. Ferber).[13] The abuse is undoubtedly an element of real child pornography, but never a part of virtual child pornography. In defining virtual child pornography, one should distinguish different types of material: *drawings* existing in the real world published on-line, *modified images* of natural persons so they can no longer be identified and *computer-generated* images ("pseudo-photographs"), in which the production of the material (with so-called digital imaging or morphing techniques) is no longer bound to taking and manipulating pictures of real people.

The CoE Convention defines "child pornography" as pornographic material that *visually depicts sexually explicit conduct* (it is not relevant whether the conduct depicted is real or simulated, i.e., including actors)[14] of one of three *types of material*: (1) a real child, (2) a person appearing to be a minor or (3) images which do not in fact involve a real person.[15] The Explanatory Report to the CoE Convention instructs that the third type includes pictures that are altered, such as morphed images of natural persons, and even generated entirely by a computer. The objects of criminal protection are therefore different: the first type focuses directly on protection against child abuse, while the other two types aim at providing protection against behaviour that *might* be used to encourage or seduce children into participating in such acts.[16] These materials, though called "child" pornography, do not depict any concrete person. The criminalization focuses on the preparatory phase of crime that *might* be committed.

The greatest fear of the proponents of such criminalization seems to be that such material will fall into the hands of children: according to one scenario, a child could be emotionally or otherwise psychologically hurt; according to a second scenario, a child could take it as normal activity and would more easily fall prey to a child molester ("grooming").

While it is clear that protection against child abuse (material depicting real children) is a legitimate goal of a state's criminal law intervention, it remains unclear whether providing criminal protection against behaviour that *might* provoke criminal activity is a legitimate reason for criminalisation – we punish an act that *might* represent *encouragement* and *seduction* to possible criminal activity in the future. The intent of an offender to commit further crimes in the future, i.e., to abuse a

[13] 458 U.S. 747 (1982).

[14] See the Explanatory Report to the Convention on Cybercrime, Point 100.

[15] The CoE Convention, Article 9.

[16] The Explanatory Report to the Convention on Cybercrime, Paragraphs 93 and 102.

concrete child, should be an essential part of a more balanced criminalization of virtual child pornography.

The criminalization of virtual child pornography thus instrumentalizes criminal law. The criminal law becomes a risk management tool, since its focus shifts from a past event to a (possible) future event on a basis of a very unclear causal link. Such provisions thus encroach on "the freedom to engage in a substantial amount of lawful speech"[17] and criminalise thoughts. They also change the purpose, if not the very idea, of criminal law. The criminalization of virtual child pornography changes criminal law into a mere symbolic tool for expression and protection of public morals. In this regard, it also breaches the *ultima ratio* principle of criminal law.

There clearly exists confusion in the reasoning of the virtual child pornography prohibition. Is it a concrete child, the idea/dignity of children or the morals of children that we are trying to protect? Human dignity has been recognized as an object of penal protection in criminal law theory, but only the human dignity of a concrete and not of an abstract person. Morals also cannot directly be the object of penal protection nor the indignation people might experience when encountering such material. The pragmatic argument that it is difficult to distinguish real child images from virtual ones also does not carry plausible theoretical value. Crime investigation has never been a simple endeavour and digital environment investigations are no exception.

In defining types of child pornographic material, the Framework Decision on child pornography is more balanced. A member state may exclude from criminal liability: (1) images of children having *reached the age of sexual consent* that are produced and possessed with their *consent* and solely for their own *private use* (for production and possession), (2) images of a real person appearing to be a child that was *in fact 18 years* of age and (3) *virtual* child pornography that is produced and possessed by the producer solely for his or her own *private use*.[18]

The criminalization of extreme and violent pornography is similar to virtual child pornography to the extent that it criminalizes acts without victims. However, it is also a very different scenario since it criminalises acts of consenting adults. Applying criminal law in such cases raises all the doubts mentioned above and also raised by content control strategies. These strategies apply only to a limited number of crimes, but grant law enforcement powers across types of conduct that should stay in the domain of privacy. The effects of internet filtering are very much known: it is flawed, it raises human rights concerns and, in a long term, it stifles innovation and creativity.

---

[17] See Ashcroft v. Free Speech Coalition, 122 S. Ct. 1389 (2002).

[18] Article 3, paragraph 2 of the Council Framework Decision 2004/68/JHA on combating the sexual exploitation of children and child pornography.

2. Infringement of IP rights

The criminalization of infringements of intellectual property (IP) rights is the next example of a disproportionate criminal law reaction in protecting perfectly legitimate interests. Empirical research, for instance, conducted among graduate students at the Faculty of Law, University of Ljubljana, on downloading copyrighted material showed that accessing such material via Torrents is a part of the teenage subculture and a learning process of how to use the Internet and PC. The most disturbing fact that the research showed was that the Slovene Criminal Code (KZ) criminalised the vast majority of internet users in the attempt to protect copyright and related rights. Namely, the criminal offence of unauthorized use of copyrighted material[19] can be committed by mere possession of copyright material. The only limitation was a "high total market value" of the material.[20]

As theorists have persuasively shown,[21] the problem of IP infringements in the digital environment is a temporary one. "Always on" connections are making it easier to subscribe to a database containing such material than to download the material and be a database manager. They have also shown that the damage caused by P2P technologies is dubious, since types of users are manifold: some may use it for downloading material that is no longer protected by copyright laws; others may download the material only to test it in order to proceed with a purchase; many download the material but never have the chance to check it at all.

Furthermore, a recent Dutch study (*Huygen et al.*, 2008) on the cultural and economic benefits of file sharing music, film and games showed that the economic implications of file sharing for the level of welfare in the Netherlands are strongly positive in both short and long terms. File sharing provides consumers with access to a broad range of cultural products, which typically raises welfare.

The general trend in the criminal law protection of copyright and related rights is shifting in the direction of higher punitiveness. The CoE Convention, as the first binding instrument, was still reasonable in the protection of intellectual property rights. It binds the signatories to criminalize infringements if they are committed intentionally and on a commercial scale. However, subsequent EU attempts to strengthen the protection of copyright and related rights are raising concerns. A French proposal for a "three-strike scheme" whereby persistent infringements of IP rights would be sanctioned by cutting off subscriptions can only be described as an overreaction to the problem, leading to the abuse of repressive power of the state. Proposals of a contri-

---

[19] The Slovene Criminal Code, Article 159 ("Unauthorized use of copyright work").

[20] The Slovene Criminal Code (KZ) was subsequently changed in this regard. The new Criminal Code (KZ-1), which entered into force in November 1, 2008, does not criminalize mere unauthorized possession of copyright work. It additionally requires the intent to sell the copyright work (Article 148 KZ-1).

[21] For instance Lessig, 2004.

bution from ISPs that enable connectivity to P2P in order to compensate damage to the content industry also raise doubts. The most elaborate EU proposal has taken the criminal law protection of copyright and related rights even further.

A proposed *EU directive on criminal measures aimed at ensuring the enforcement of intellectual property rights* (so-called Second Intellectual Property Rights Enforcement Directive or "IPRED2")[22], which aims at complementing the "IPR Enforcement Directive" ("IPRED")[23] fails to provide consumers with clear legal guidance regarding the use of copyright material on the web. The most controversial part requires Member States to ensure that all intentional infringements of an intellectual property right on a commercial scale, and attempting, aiding or abetting and inciting such infringements, are treated as criminal offences (IPRED2, Article 3). Mere criminalisation of incitement to infringement of IP rights overturns the balance in the national criminal codes of member states that do not even criminalize inciting far more serious offences. Additionally, the prescribed penalties are severe: at least 4 years imprisonment and, additionally, at least 300,000€ fine for an aggravated form of the criminal offence and at least 100.000€ fine for the basic form of the offence.

Increasing the severity of punishment in the criminal law protection of copyright and related rights, according to Sieber (2008: 153), is accompanied by a strong tendency to cover preliminary stages of infringement of copyright and related rights by means of civil law. It means not only criminalizing the preparatory phases of IP rights infringements, but also a tendency to protect digital rights management systems, technological measures that protect digital goods against unauthorized reproduction, and to protect conditional access systems. Since "code is the law" (Lessig, 1999), a digital environment enables technical solutions which allow, for instance, only authorized persons to remotely update purchased software. Or, for instance, if you have an iPhone that enables access to anything Apple deems objectionable, Apple can block it. This practice of "engineering-out" IP right infringements dangerously threatens the open nature of the internet (*Zittrain*, 2008).

3. Illegal access ("Hacking")

The CoE Convention and the EU Framework Decision on attacks against information systems[24] oblige signatories and member states to criminalize acts against the confidentiality, integrity and availability of computer data and systems (so-

---

[22] COM(2006)0168 final, 2005/0127(COD), April 26, 2006.

[23] Directive 2004/48/EC of the European Parliament and of the Council of 29 April 2004 on the enforcement of intellectual property rights. Official Journal of the European Union L 157 of 30 April 2004.

[24] EU Council Framework Decision 2005/222/JHA on attacks against information systems of 24.2.2005, OJ L 69, 16.3.2005.

called "C.I.A. offences"). The criminal offence of illegal access to the whole or any part of "a computer system" (the CoE Convention) or "an information system" (the EU Framework Decision) has remained one of the most controversial in terms of disproportionate substantive criminal law provisions.

The main argument against criminalization of access to an information system is that it stifles future development of computer (security) software. So-called "penetration tests" are regularly used to identify gaps and vulnerabilities of computer systems and networks. The criminalisation hence prohibits the early stages of software development process. It shows that concepts developed for the off-line environment cannot be used for the digital world by mere analogy. Access to a computer system perhaps *primae faciae* resembles unauthorised access to physical space, but access to an information system actually resembles the work of an architect in the "real" world. Both may be regarded as creators of the protected environment. Similarly to the criminalisation of virtual child pornography, criminal law reaches further into the preparatory phases of committing a crime. However, unfortunately, the criminalization of access to an information system in cases of computer software development coincides with the phase of creating the very digital space that we are trying to protect. The very creation of new computer software is ordinarily connected to some form of access to another computer software or information system in order to provide interoperability or interconnectivity.

The signatories of the CoE Convention did not reach complete agreement on the criminalization of illegal access to a computer system. The current provision thereby allows countries to criminalize mere illegal access[25] without any additional conditions. Such a "margin of appreciation" has led some countries to set additional restrictions, such as, for instance, the restriction that the offence of illegally accessing an information system be committed by infringing security measures or that the perpetrator acts with the intent of committing further acts (Sieber, 2008: 142).

4. Modes of execution (*actus reus*)

The substantive criminal law concepts of "possession", "procuring" and "supplying" were created for the physical environment. The digital environment considerably changes the meaning of what it means to "possess", to "procure" or to "supply" prohibited material. The nature of the internet as a network of networks means that "material" resides on different computers (servers) and is constantly moving. Additionally, supposedly disputed "material" is always disentangled into packets that travel separately and take different routes.

At the beginning of internet development, criminal law theory required that a person had to download material in order to be recognised as being a "possessor"

[25] The U.K. Computer Misuse Act 1990 criminalizes mere illegal access to a computer system.

of the material. A form of permanent storage of the data was required. Mere surfing on the Internet was not considered to be a form of a temporary "possession" of the displayed material. Accordingly, surfing a web page with child pornography images, for instance, was not be considered a child pornography offence.

It became evident that criminalizing only the supply of prohibited material would not eradicate the disputed content. The demand for prohibited material should be prohibited as well. By focusing on the purely technical aspects of digital technology it became clear that surfing the Internet technically means that the user's devices more or less automatically saves digital material in some from. One always leaves a "digital fingerprint". For instance, when browsing the Internet the computer automatically stores data in the so-called cache memory (i.e. RAM memory that is set aside as specialized buffer storage that is continually updated), or, for instance, cookies are almost automatically installed on a user's hard disc during web page browsing. These examples show how IT blurs the definition of "possession" that was created for the off-line environment.

IT also blurs once straightforward demarcations of possession from the "procurement" or "supply" of digital material. Some countries prohibit the supply and procurement of controversial material but not also its possession. So, while it is more or less possible to differentiate between illegally possessing firearms from procuring them, it is difficult, for instance, to distinguish the two in the case of file sharing technology. When one is downloading material in P2P networks, one is simultaneously making it available for the use of others. The very essence of P2P technology is that users enable access to the disc spaces of other users. This kind of voluntary permission cannot be disputed. However, the mere use of file sharing technology may lead to "procurement" or "supply" of the illegal digital material. Illegal copy in My Shared folder (Kazaa) automatically means that the user is "procuring" or "supplying" the material – "mere" possession is not possible.

The question, therefore, is whether a user can be held criminally responsible for content that is temporarily stored in the cache memory of his or her computer? For instance, in a case in which a user has coincidentally visited a homepage containing child pornography but did not delete the temporary storage? It could be criminalized as a criminal act of omission, but such criminalisation is reaching too far in the domain of the free use of the IT. The EU Framework Decision on child pornography is balanced in this regard, since it obliges member states to prohibit the mere possession of child pornography only if the offence is committed intentionally (Article 3).

C. Challenges of criminal procedure

A lack of substantial criminal law adaptation has usually been to the detriment of the efficiency of law enforcement: if the substantive rules had been adopted, the offenders would have been prosecuted according to the principle of legality. However, non-adapted criminal procedure provisions, in contrast, have been to the detriment of fundamental liberties. Procedural rules were tailored for collecting physical (not digital, intangible and transient) evidence and eyewitness testimony. Their use in the digital environment requires some refinement in order to prevent the excessive power of law enforcement.

New rules of criminal procedure have been created to some extent in most European countries. Nevertheless, there is a vast discrepancy between jurisdictions. In contrast to the common law countries, where a higher frequency of cases has led the judiciary to tailor a substantial amount of new detailed procedural rules (Walden, 2007), at least in Slovenia, for instance, only recently a proposed Act Amending the Criminal Procedure Act (ZKP-K) has been prepared to address digital and network environment investigations.

An analysis of the (over)reaction of the criminal justice complex to cybercrime in relation to the rules of criminal procedure has to consider two opposing trends: information societies' increasing dependence on the digitisation of business, management and infrastructure regulation processes, which in turn renders them highly susceptible (vulnerable) to cybercrime, on the one hand, and IT development that gives law enforcement new surveillance powers, on the other. The art of finding a balance between law enforcement investigative powers and the protection of fundamental liberties has become an even more delicate process in information societies than it was ever before. IT is evolving rapidly, capabilities such as processing speed and memory capacity are improving at exponential rates (according to Moor's law of the long-term trend in the history of computing hardware).

Societies' increasing dependence on digitised data makes digital forensics (also called cyber forensics, or computer and network forensics) more and more important. It answers questions of how to collect intangible and transient data, how to analyse them and how to preserve the collected digital information in a legally acceptable form. In spite of the "electronic footprints omnipresence"[26] the police and legally trained personnel in the criminal justice system are still hesitant to collect intangible transient data. According to research on digital forensics (Selinšek, 2008) conducted for the Slovene criminal justice system, criminal court judges do not share enthusiasm for digitisation. They are reluctant to use digital evidence and are inclined to rely on conventional evidence. In spite of widespread digitalisation in Slovene society, digital evidence still represents an insignificant share in all police investigations. The Slovene police filed almost 500,000 criminal charges in the period 2001 – 2006, but only 212 contained digital evidence (0.043 percent) (*Selinšek*, 2008: 51). It is difficult to ascertain the reasons for such reluctance but it seems that sophisticated networked IT is still very poorly understood by lawyers.

---

26 Companies store the majority of information in digital form and by some estimates digital information represents as much as 90 percent of all relevant information.

In order to employ digital evidence, digital forensic activities should be regulated. However, the question of "who can act as a cyber forensic expert?" remains unanswered. With the exception of the US and a few EU member states,[27] expertise in digital forensics is insufficiently regulated. There is no registration of forensic practitioners and only basic guidance on handling digital evidence exists. In continental legal systems, digital forensics is entrusted to expert witnesses and thus regulated by national expert witness administrative regimes. The principle of free evaluation of evidence means that a judge can call on an expert witness to technically evaluate a certain fact. However, due to a lack of understanding of IT and its capabilities it is not very likely that an expert witness will be called upon to deliver expert evidence in the first place. Another shortcoming in digital forensics is thus a lack of appropriate training of law enforcement personnel. Because prosecutors and judges are not familiar with IT, they are inclined to rely on what they already know. In cases in which such training exists, it is only offered by forensic tools manufacturers, who are inevitability pursuing their own agenda.[28]

Cyber-forensics techniques encompass three groups of activities: (1) cyber-surveillance, (2) surveillance interception and (3) search and seizure (Walden, 2007). The rolc of communication service providers (CSPs) in state-instigated *cyber-surveillance* remains controversial. CSPs are obliged to perform state imposed obligations. They act as a buffer for invasive privacy intrusions of the state, on the one hand, and as an extended "long arm of justice", on the other. Additionally, they have their own commercial interest agenda that leads them into a voluntary cyber-surveillance. They are inclined, for instance, to engage in excessive spying on their clients by profiling, creating databases and monitoring the behaviour patterns of their customers. An individual is under the gaze of not only the state but also private entities, which are jointly tightening "the surveillant assemblage".

Surveillance interception is a process of collecting data from CSPs. An absence of a data definition has raised some dilemmas. The conceptual division between content data (data transmitted by suspects) and communications data (data generated by CSPs) has become theoretically flawed. For instance, is a sequence number of a packet communications or content data? There are disparities between definitions of data among EU and other countries. The vast amount of communications data being created by new IT devices also shows that communications data can sometimes be more informative about an individual than content data. Registered daily visits to a church or a mosque, for instance, in one's smart phone location-based device, is more informative than a one sentence self-description saying one is a Christian or a Muslim.

---

[27] See Walden, 2007.

[28] For instance, training provided by the Cybex Company and its "The European Certificate on Cybercrime and Electronic Evidence (ECCE)" (Cybex, 2008).

There are several further challenges that data retention regulation should answer: what kind of communications data should CSPs intercept: transmitted or (and) stored data, data of which they are in possession or also data they are capable of obtaining? Should only public service (network) providers or also private ones retain data? Who should bear the costs of interception? According to the EU Data Retention Directive, providers of ("only") publicly available electronic communications services and public communications networks within the jurisdiction of member states are obliged to retain the data. The obligation extends to traffic data, location data, subscriber's data and facts and circumstances with regard to unsuccessful call attempts. Bearing in mind that the vast amount of data retained pertains to every user, the directive jeopardizes fundamental rights and human liberties (especially, the right to privacy and the presumption of innocence).

The disproportionate nature of the Data Retention Directive to a large extent follows the vague justifications set in its preamble. The surveillance net-widening effect that it is creating is a result of various goals: it is expected to be an efficient measure to tackle *obstacles to the internal EU market* for electronic communications, *organised crime*, *fight against terrorism* and also enable investigation, detection and prosecution of *serious crime* (defined, vaguely, as criminalized by each member state).

Search and seizure are coercive investigatory powers that enable obtaining data from a suspect. The new methods of collecting digital evidence have triggered a need for new legal standards. IT tends to divide the process of search and seizure into two steps (Kerr, 2005). The police first execute a physical search to seize computer hardware and later execute a second electronic search to obtain the data from a seized computer storage device. The failure of the law to account for the two-stage process of computer searches and seizures has been to the detriment of fundamental liberties. A physical search has in practice been more or less automatically followed by an electronic search, without any judicial overview. Similarly, the extent of a warrant's entry authorisation in cases of domestic wireless networks has still not been sufficiently addressed.

The part of the CoE Convention that deals with search and seizure grants law enforcement impressive powers. If the authorities have grounds to believe that the data sought is stored in *another* computer system (or part of it) in its territory and such data is lawfully accessible from or available to the initial system, the authorities are supposed to be able expeditiously to extend the search to the other system (Article 19). In the light of "on-line searches" that enable deep, remote and secret intrusions into the privacy of IT users, the provision of Article 19 is overreaching.[29]

---

[29] Similarly, in this regard Sieber (2008: 161) warns that the CoE Convention was elaborated between 1997 and 2000 and that the available investigation tools have rapidly changed in the meantime. He thus recommends an update of the procedural tools in the CoE Convention.

IV. Conclusion

The dilemma between the problem (cybercrime) and the reaction to "the problem" (criminal justice system's response) shows that the reaction to the problem has become a problem on its own. The overextension of criminal law jeopardizes civil liberties (human rights concerns), our privacy, freedom of expression, freedom of association and fair trial. It has an impact on the free use of the Internet and research shows how the disproportionate reaction to the problem, for instance in the form of data retention,[30] have reduced IT usage (public policy concerns).

The police, the justice system and private enterprises network and organize in order to control online activities through new nodes and clusters and are forming what has been called the "surveillant assemblage" (Haggerty and Ericson, 2000). The expansion of "dataveillance" (Clarke, 1987) takes advantage of new surveillance technologies, such as mechanisms to monitor, screen and analyse records of billions of telephone and email communications; localisation possibilities ("positioning") determine the location of an individual or create a movement profile (with, for instance, GSM triangulation, electronic toll payment records, GPS technology, wireless networks, radio-frequency identity tags); on-line search and seizures can remotely and secretly monitor a suspect's online activities, password and email, the computer's camera and microphone (Brown and Korff, 2009). Intelligence-led policing (Lemieux, 2008) has become the new prototype of policing styles and boundaries of military, intelligence and police intelligence that are blurring render our fundamental rights highly vulnerable.

Cybercrime prevention strategies, substantive criminal law changes and adjustments of the rules of criminal procedure form a part of processes and shifts in criminal justice policy heading towards more intense cyber-surveillance. These changes thus have to be observed as a part of a larger picture, only as the tips of the iceberg of the "surveillance society".

References

- BARRACUDA NETWORKS. 2007. *Annual Spam Report* [online]. [Accessed 15 May 2009]. Available from World Wide Web: <http://www.barracudanetworks.com/ns/news_and_events/index.php?nid=232>.
- BLOSS, W. 2007. Escalating U.S. Police Surveillance after 9/11: an Examination of Causes and Effects. *Surveillance & Society, Special Issue on 'Surveillance and Criminal Justice' Part 1* [online]. 4 (3), [Accessed 15 May 2009], pp. 208-228. Available from World Wide Web: <http://www.surveillance-and-society.org>.

[30] A research conducted by German research organisation FORSA (2008) shows the effects of data retention: 73% of population has heard about the data retention, 11% of the Internet users did not use the phone and e-mail because of that, 6% considers that they received less info and even 52% claim that they would not use telecommunications services for discussion with a pharmacist, psychotherapist or marriage broker.

- BRIDIS, T. and J. SOLOMON (2006). Police Got Phone Data from Brokers. *ABC News* [online]. June 20, [Accessed 27 June 2008]. Available from World Wide Web: <http://abcnews.go.com/Business/wireStory?.html>.
- BROWN, I. and D. KORFF. 2009. Terrorism and the Proportionality of Internet Surveillance. *European Journal of Criminology*, 6 (2), pp. 119-134.
- CARTER, D. 2004. *Law Enforcement Intelligence: A Guide for State, Local, and Tribal Law Enforcement*. Washington, DC: National Institute of Justice.
- CHENG, J. 2007. *Report: 95 percent of all e-mail has that spammy smell* [online]. [Accessed 15 May 2009]. Available from World Wide Web: <http://arstechnica.com/old/content/2007/12/report-95-percent-of-all-e-mail-has-that-spammy-smell.ars>.
- CLARKE, R. 1087. *Information Technology and Dataveillance* [online]. [Accessed 10 July 2009]. Available from World Wide Web: <http://www.rogerclarke.com/DV/CACM88.html>.
- COLE, D. and J. LOBEL. 2007. *Less Safe, Less Free: Why We Are Losing the War on Terror*. New York: New Press.
- COUNCIL OF EUROPE. 2007. *Octopus Interface 2007 »Cooperation against Cybercrime«*, 11-12 June 2007, Palais de l'Europe, Strasbourg, France [online]. [Accessed 14 December 2007]. Available from World Wide Web: <http://www.coe.int/t/e/legal_affairs/legal_coopeation/combating_economic_crime/3_technical_cooperation/CYBER/Octopus_if_2007.asp#TopOfPage>.
- COUNCIL OF EUROPE. 2008a. *Octopus Interface 2008*, 1-2 April 2008, Strasbourg, France [online]. [Accessed 28 February 2009]. Available from World Wide Web: <http://www.coe.int/t/dghl/cooperation/economiccrime/cybercrime/cy_activity_Interface 2008/Interface2008_en.asp>.
- COUNCIL OF EUROPE. 2008b. *Octopus Interface 2008 Conference Report.* [online]. [Accessed 28 February 2009]. Available from World Wide Web: <http://www.coe.int/t/dghl/cooperation/economiccrime/cybercrime/T-CY/T-CY_2008(04)-Finalen.pdf>.
- COUNCIL OF EUROPE. 2009. *Octopus Interface 2009 Conference*, 10-11 March 2009, Strasbourg. [online]. [Accessed 5 March 2009]. Available from World Wide Web: <http://www.coe.int/t/dghl/cooperation/economiccrime/cybercrime/cy%20activity%20interface%202009/Interface2009_en.asp>.
- CYBEX, 2008. *The European Certificate on Cybercrime and Electronic Evidence (ECCE) Project* [online]. [Accessed 20 August 2009]. Available from World Wide Web: <http://www.cybex.es/ecce/>.
- DORIA, A. 2007. What do the Words "Internet Security" Mean? *In*: W. KLEINWŒCHTER, ed. *The Power of Ideas: Internet Governance in a Global Multi-Stakeholder Environment*. Berlin: Marketing für Deutschland GmbH, pp. 197-207.
- EUROPEAN DIGITAL RIGHTS. 2009. *European Digital Rights' website* [online]. [Accessed 25 February 2009]. Available from World Wide Web: <http://www.edri.org/>.
- FORSA, 2008. *Meinungen der Bundesbürger zur Vorratsdatenspeicherung* [online]. [Accessed 10 June 2009]. Available from World Wide Web: <http://www.vorratsdatenspeicherung.de/images/forsa_2008-06-03.pdf>.
- GARFINKEL, S. 2000. *Database Nation: The Death of Privacy in the 21st Century.* Cambridge, Mass.: O'Reilly & Associates.

- GAGNON, B. 2008. Cyberwars and cybercrimes. *In*: S. LEMAN-LANGLOIS, ed. *Technocrime: Technology, Crime and Social Control*. Cullompton [England], Portland, Or.: Willan Publishing, pp. 46-65.
- GERMAN WORKING GROUP ON DATA RETENTION (AK Vorrat). 2009. *German Working Group on Data Retention website* [online]. [Accessed 25 February 2009]. Available from World Wide Web: <http://www.vorratsdatenspeicherung.de/content/view/298/55/lang,en/>.
- GRABOSKY, P. 2001. Computer Crime: A Criminological Overview. *Forum on Crime and Society*, 1 (1), pp. 35-53.
- HAGGERTY, K.D. and R.V. ERICSON. 2000. The surveillant assemblage. *British Journal of Sociology*, 51(4), pp. 605-622.
- HUYGEN, A. et al. 2008. *Ups and Downs: Economic and Cultural Effects of File Sharing on Music, Film and Games*. TNO-rapport 34782 [online]. [Accessed 10 May 2009]. Available from World Wide Web: <http://www.tno.nl/content.cfm?context=markten&content=publicatie&laag1=182&laag2=1&item_id=473&Taal=2>.
- KERR, O.S. 2005. Digital Evidence and the New Criminal Procedure. *Columbia Law Review*, 15, pp. 279-318.
- LEMIEUX, F. 2008. Information technology and criminal intelligence: a comparative perspective. *In*: S. LEMAN-LANGLOIS, ed. *Technocrime: Technology, Crime and Social Control*. Cullompton [England], Portland, Or.: Willan Publishing, pp. 139-168.
- LEMAN-LANGLOIS, S. 2008. Introduction: technocrime. *In*: S. LEMAN-LANGLOIS, ed., *Technocrime: Technology, Crime and Social Control*. Cullompton [England], Portland, Or.: Willan Publishing, pp. 1-13.
- LESSIG, L. 1999. *Code and Other Laws of Cyberspace*. New York: Basic Books.
- LESSIG, L. 2004. *Free Culture: how big media uses technology and the law to lock down culture and control creativity*. New York: Penguin Press.
- MCGUIRE, M. 2007. *Hypercrime: A Geometry of Virtual Harm*. London: GlassHouse.
- NHAN, J. and L. HUEY. 2008. Policing through nodes, clusters and bandwidth. *In*: S. LEMAN-LANGLOIS, ed. *Technocrime: Technology, Crime and Social Control*. Cullompton [England], Portland, Or.: Willan Publishing, pp. 66-87.
- O'HARROW, R. 2005. *No Place To Hide*. New York: Free Press.
- PETERSON, M. 2005. *Intelligence-Led Policing: The New Intelligence Architecture*. Washington, DC: Bureau of Justice Assistance.
- ROWAN, D. 2006. Britain is flooding the world with spam. TimesOnline [online]. 24 January 2004, [Accessed 15 May 2009]. Available from World Wide Web: <http://www.timesonline.co.uk/tol/news/uk/article1002172.ece>.
- SELINŠEK, L. 2008. Digitalna forenzika v kazenskih postopkih. *In*: L. SELINŠEK, ed. *Digitalna forenzika v kazenskih postopkih*. Ljubljana: GV Založba, pp.13-64.
- SIEBER, U. 2008. Mastering Complexity in the Global Cyberspace. *In*: M. Delmas-Marty, M. Pieth and U. Sieber, eds. *Les chemins de l'harmonisation pénale*. Paris: Société de Législation Comparéé.

- SYMANTEC. 2006. *Cybercrime Continues to Rise* (Report from April 2006) [online]. [Accessed 2 February 2009]. Available from World Wide Web: <http://www.symantec.com/business/resources/articles/article.jsp?aid=internet_security_threat_report_cybercrime#introduction>.
- SYMANTEC. 2008. *Report on the Underground Economy (July 07–June 08)* [online]. [Accessed 2 February 2009]. Available from World Wide Web: <http://eval.symantec.com/mktginfo/enterprise/white_papers/whitepaper_underground_economy_report_11-2008-14525717.en-us.pdf>.
- ZITTRAIN, J. 2008. *The Future of the Internet and How to Stop It*. New Haven [Conn.]: Yale University Press.
- WALDEN, I. 2007. *Computer Crime and Digital Investigations*. Oxford et al.: Oxford University Press.
- WALL, D.S. 2007. *Cybercrime: The Transformation of Crime in the Information Age*. Cambridge, Malden: Polity Press.

Soumyo Moitra

A Risk Analysis Model for Internet Security Management for Organizations

The decision about the best network security level is important for many organizations. This paper suggests an approach for finding this level. Based on cost minimization, the model uses data on the cost of different levels of security, the expected damage given a security level and the rate of network attacks the organization experiences. As cost of security increases, the expected damage decreases and it is shown that an optimal security level will generally exist where total cost to the organization is minimized. The optimal point varies for different scenarios which reflect different organizational conditions. Four cost/damage scenarios were developed and the numerical results are presented. The model itself is relatively simple, and the major challenge is the collection of reliable data.

I. Introduction

This paper presents a normative model to assist organizations to decide on the most appropriate security level to protect their network systems and information assets. Today, almost all organizations are not only connected to the Internet and possibly to other networks (intranets and extranets), but the intensity of the activity on the networks is rapidly increasing. As such, they are constantly vulnerable to cyber attacks, network intrusions and cybercrimes. It is therefore not a surprise that organizations generally take precautions against such possible breaches. Since network operations is often vital for an organization and since it may have valuable data on its systems, the budget for security is significant for many organizations and can be extremely high for some. As is the case for all business decisions, there is always the need to justify the network security budget, and for any organization, it is important to identify the most appropriate level since otherwise, it would lead to inefficiencies in resource allocation (Camp and Lewis, Caulkins, et al., Jasquith and Shostack and Stewart). The development of the security budget is an on-going process as the security needs of an organization has to be reviewed constantly. Thus it is useful to have a decision model to help with the decision-making.

II. Model Development

The issues involved in developing a decision model to help in security decisions and investments have been discussed in many papers and some books (Arora, et al., Cashell, CISCO, Gordon and Loeb, McLean and Brown, Moitra, and Paquet and Saxe) A review of the relevant literature may be found in Moitra (2008). Here we describe a decision analysis-based model and discuss the results from numerical estimation.

The model considers the levels of network security (*s*) as a spectrum of values from low to high, which may be measured along a scale or as a positive number. Here we consider three basic roles of network security: prevention, protection and deterrence. Prevention means that a cyber attack was detected and successfully stopped, so that it was prevented from causing any damage. Protection means that the attack was detected but could not be fully stopped. However, steps were taken to mitigate the potential damage that could have been caused. Deterrence refers to the overall effect of reducing the number of attacks directed against the organization.

Characterization of the security level *s* can be complex. We assume that its value increases with the security that the organization has, but measuring this is complicated by the fact that there are a wide range of security measures and different security measures protect different things to greater or lesser extent. Any security posture of an organization is a composite of many elements, such as software and hardware systems such as virus detectors, firewalls, patches, intrusion detection/prevention devices, and so on. It can be difficult to compare the relative amounts of security each combination may provide and to assign a level to each. However, we assume that for a particular organization the decision makers can evaluate the different security alternatives that the organization realistically has, and depending on its network as well as the assets it has to protect, it can assign a level to each alternative. Without loss of generality, we shall assume here that for each security system the organization is considering, it will assign a value on a scale from 1 to 10 to it.

Of course, each security alternative will have a cost C(s) associated with it, and we shall assume that the alternatives are efficient (in the economic sense) and C(s) increases monotonically with s. We also assume that the expected damages that the organization may suffer from a cyber attack after security system of level s has be deployed is d(s) and that d(s) decreases monotonically with s. The total expected damage over a given time period D(s) will be this expected damage per attack multiplied by the rate at which the organization experiences cyber attacks (n(s)). In general, the attack rate will be a function of s, because we are assuming that higher values of s will tend to reduce the attack rate as well through deterrence. Thus $D(s) = d(s) * n(s)$. To be a little more precise, both d and n should be functions of the attack category i. Thus, $D(s) = \sum_i d(i, s) * n(i, s)$, that is, the total damage should be summed over the damages caused by each type of attack.

The optimal point, if one exists, will be the point where $Z(s) = C(s) + D(s)$ is minimized, since Z represents the total cost to the organization and where the attack category (i) is suppressed. As s increases, C increases and D decreases. As shown in Table 1, we can expect that Z will have a minimum in most realistic cases. Two types of exceptions can occur, and these will be discussed later.

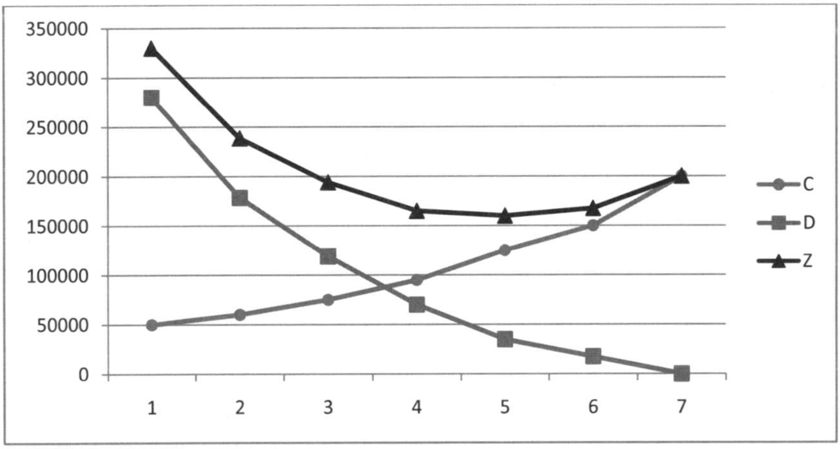

Figure 1: Plot of costs, damages and Z with respect to the security level.

A. Model Estimation

This is the basic Benefit-Cost model, and has been widely used in economics, business and policy analysis. The problems lie in estimating the costs and damage reductions. To estimate the damage reductions we have to have data on expected damages as a function of the attack category and security level, since both these factors affect the potential damage caused by a cyber attack. Some attacks cause significantly more damage than others, and the actual damage suffered (per attack) would decrease as security level increases. We assume that as the security level s increases, the probability of detection, the probability of prevention and the degree of protection will all increase, and thus the expected damage will decrease. To estimate the expected damage reduction, we need to know what the damage would have been in the absence of the security system (no security) and what the expected damage will be with the security system in place. Estimation of damages involves consideration of tangible and intangible variables. In particular, the value of the information on an organization's system can vary considerably and its estimation is often subjective. There are some suggestions in the literature on ways of doing this (Arora, et al., Gordon and Loeb), but there are still many outstanding difficulties. Here we assume that the organization has developed a methodology for doing this (as described in Moitra and Konda, for example).

We also need to have data on the rate of cyber attacks that the organization experiences. This is also not an easy variable to estimate, since most organizations do not know the true rate of attacks they incur. The data they have is the number of alerts about possible cyber attacks their security system generates. This is the sum of both false and true positives (that is, a false alert and a true attack). The organization may or may not have the count of true positives. However, in addition to that, there could be attacks that were not detected (false negatives, since they should have generated an alert). It is usually extremely difficult to know this count, and hence the true attack rate is very difficult to estimate. Here again, we assume that the organization has done some investigation and has estimated the actual attack rate it experiences.

There is the further issue of estimating the deterrence effect of security. If the security level is high, some attackers may find it too difficult to breach the defenses, and will give up. Thus the effect will be to reduce the rate of attacks the organizations faces, and this deterrence effect needs to be known. However, as with other factors related to the behavior of cyber attackers and cyber criminals, this is almost impossible to estimate directly. The most that can be done is to observe attack rates against organizations with different levels of security and examine whether, controlling for other factors, attack rates diminish as security levels increase. However, there can be many other empirical difficulties with this approach. Therefore, in this paper we do not assume any deterrence effect, but will discuss the issue again later.

Finally, we need to have data on the costs of maintaining a security level s for a given organization. Again, this is not a simple exercise, as a number of cost elements have to be considered. In addition to the purchase prices of the security components, we need to consider auxiliary hardware and software costs, installation and maintenance costs, monitoring costs and incident-handling costs. A variety of human resource (such as training) and policy-related costs may need to be included. In the case of costs, the organization would very likely have the needed data or can collect it for this purpose.

B. Analysis and Results

Once the data is collected, we can minimize Z(s) over s. In most cases, there will be a discrete set of security systems under consideration, and one can do a simple grid search over the values of s to determine which system has the lowest Z. Thus the optimization is relatively easy, if we have the data. In case there are many alternatives, and s is like a continuous variable, we can find the optimal point with any optimization package. In either case, the optimization is not difficult.

As mentioned earlier, we shall examine the case where the attack rate is independent of the security level. In the numerical example, we shall also consider attacks to be homogeneous, that is we shall consider the average attack category. The generalization to multiple attack categories is quite straight-forward.

From available literature, (mostly reports on cyber crime such as AusCERT, BJS, BERR formerly DTI, and CSI) we have constructed four scenarios as follows: high cost/low damage, high cost/high damage, low cost/low damage and low cost/high damage. The low cost scenario considered the lower values for cost of security as found in the literature. Similarly, the high cost scenario considered the higher values for costs. In reality we would expect a spectrum of costs in between these values. Similarly, reports on damages from cyber crime were reviewed, and lower and upper bounds were estimated for these scenarios. Then the optimization model was run for each of these four scenarios and the optimal level of security (Z*) for each was identified. The results are shown in Table 1.

Cost scenario	**Damage scenario**	**Z***
High	Low	3
Low	High	6
High	High	5
Low	Low	5

Table 1: Optimal level of security for cost and damage scenarios

In the high cost/low damage scenario, we see that the optimal point is on the low side, and this is what we would expect for an organization that would not lose very much through cyber attacks, and at the same time faces high security costs. At the opposite end, when costs are low and potential damages are high, the organization will naturally select a high level of security. For the next two cases, the optimal point is the same. This means that both for the high cost/high damage and for the low cost/low damage scenarios the optimal point is in between the first two extremes and are about the same. We can interpret this to imply that if potential damages from cyber attacks are estimated to be high, the organization will select a level that is higher than if damages were low, and also which is lower than if costs were low. The result for the low cost/low damage scenario can be interpreted in a similar manner.

There are two further cases that need to be considered. The optimal points obtained in the above scenarios occur under certain conditions (called the Kuhn-Tucker conditions). However, when damages decrease with s at a slower rate than costs, then the "optimal" point is actually the so-called "corner point" corresponding to the minimum level of security. We can understand this result by considering a small business with very little network assets. Then, increasing security would not be worthwhile as the assets to be protected are not valuable in the first place. The business would end up spending more on security than it would expect to lose through possible cyber attacks. Thus the most appropriate level would be minimum security.

The second case is the exact opposite where damages decrease with s at a faster rate than costs. For such an organization, it would always be worthwhile to spend more on security, as the benefits from reduced expected damages will always outweigh the costs. We can think of financial institutions and other organizations with sensitive data as examples of such organizations. Thus the most appropriate solution for them would be the maximum level of security money can buy.

III. Conclusions

In this paper we have developed a model to help determine the most appropriate security level for any organization. The model is a traditional benefit-cost model and we have illustrated the model with several examples that highlight the range of scenarios we might encounter in real situations. We have identified those cases where an "optimal" solution may be estimated, and also those cases where solution might be either minimum security or maximum security.

The modeling and the solution methodology are not difficult, but the key problem is to collect the required data. In this paper we have briefly outlined possible methodologies for obtaining the data, but there may still be issues with potential errors and biases in the estimates. It is important for future research to develop better estimation methodologies. Another area for future work is to develop alternative models that can be estimated more robustly, can utilize available data and is useful and practical at the same time.

The model presented here assumed that the security level of an organization did not have any deterrence effect. That is, the security level does not affect the attack rate the organization experiences. However, it is possible that the security level does affect the attack rate, and there could be two possibilities depending on the type of attackers targeting the organization. For some attackers, a higher security would be a deterrent and the attack coming from them will be reduced. However, it is possible that a higher security will act as an inducement to some attackers who are interested in proving their skills at cyber attacks and intrusions. For this group, a higher level may actually increase the number of attacks they launch. It is important to consider this possibility, but a model that takes this into account requires data on the numbers of hackers in each group and how they react to security levels. Currently the prospect of obtaining such data appears remote, but future research should keep this in mind and develop appropriate models.

References:

- ARORA, A., et al. – Measuring the Risk-Based Value of IT Security Solutions. IT Professional, Nov-Dec 2004, 35-42.
- AusCERT. 2007. The 2005 Australian Computer Crime and Security Survey.
- BERR 2008. Information Security Breaches Survey: Technical Report. BERR, UK.

- BJS 2005. National *Cybercrime Survey.* Bureau of Justice Statistics, Department of Justice, US.
- CAMP, L.J. and LEWIS, S. – Economics of Information Security. Kluwer, Boston, 2004.
- CASHELL, B. et al. The Economic Impact of Cyber-Attacks. CRS Report for Congress. 2004.
- CAULKINS, J., HOUGH, E.D., MEAD, N.R. and OSMAN, H. – Optimizing Investments in Security Countermeasures: A Practical Tool for Fixed Budgets. IEEE Security & Privacy, 24-27, Sep./Oct. 2007.
- CISCO SYSTEMS - The Return on Investments for Network Security. White Paper, 2001.
- CSI 2009. The 2009 CSI Computer Crime and Security Survey.
- GORDON, L.A. and LOEB, M.P. – Managing Cybersecurity Resources. McGraw-Hill, N.Y., 2006.
- JAQUITH, A. – Security Metrics: Replacing Fear, Uncertainty and Doubt. Addison-Wesley, 2007.
- MCLEAN, G and BROWN, J. – Determining the ROI in IT Security (Available Online)
- MOITRA, S. D. Managing Risks from Cybercrime: Internet Policy and Security Management for Organizations. Research in Brief, Vol.39, Max-Planck-Institute for Criminal Law, Freiburg, 2008.
- MOITRA, S. D. and S.L. KONDA . A Simulation Model for Managing Survivability of Networked Information Systems. SEI/CERT Report, Carnegie-Mellon University, 2001.
- PAQUET, C. and SAXE, W. – The Business Case for Network Security: Advocacy, Governance and ROI. Cisco Press, 2004.
- SHOSTACK, A. and STEWART, A. – The New School of Information Security. Addison-Wesley, Upper Saddle River, NJ, 2008.

Dominik Brodowski

EU Actions on Cybercrime and Cybercrime Investigations

How recent proposals for framework decisions promote a path towards a genuinely European law – and practice? – on criminal procedure*

While the EU legal framework for combating cybercrime used to lag behind the standard set forth by the Council of Europe Cybercrime Convention, current legislative actions create unprecedented opportunities – and risks – in the field of cybercrime investigations. Furthermore, the upcoming Stockholm Programme as political framework and the Lisbon Treaty as legal framework provide for an even closer European cooperation, which may ultimately lead to cybercrime investigations and prosecutions on a genuinely European level. This broad overview of the Europeanization of substantive criminal law, mutual legal assistance and Europeanized cybercrime investigations puts special emphasis on the application of the principle of proportionality.

I. A Turning Point in Time

European Union (EU) law on cybercrime is at a turning point: while the *Council Framework Decision 2005/222/JHA of 24 February 2005 on attacks against information systems* (OJ L 69, 16.03.2005, p. 67) was more or less a "copy & paste" of the Council of Europe (CoE) *Convention on Cybercrime* (CETS No. 185, "*CoE Cybercrime Convention*") of 2001, recent Commission proposals call for unprecedented requirements to national laws to provide for specific *investigation and surveillance techniques*. An updated European Evidence Warrant II will relax requirements regarding the obtaining of evidence in another member state. Furthermore, the *Lisbon Treaty amending the Treaty on European Union and the Treaty establishing the European Community* (OJ C 306, 17.12.2007, p. 1, "*Lisbon Treaty*") allows for a true Europeanization of cybercrime investigations. This shows the EU has surpassed the CoE as *the* driving force towards reform of criminal laws and criminal procedure relating to cybercrime.

The following, broad overview of the Europeanization of substantive criminal law, mutual legal assistance between the member states of the EU, and European-

---

*This contribution reflects the state of EU actions as of August 2009. For more recent developments, e.g. relating to the entry into force of the Lisbon Treaty on 1 December 2009, the agreement on the Stockholm Programme on 11 December 2009 (Council Document 17024/09), and the updated Proposal for a Directive on combating the sexual abuse, sexual exploitation of children and child pornography (COM[2010] 94 final), please refer to my presentation available in the proceedings of LinuxTag 2010 and at SSRN: http://ssrn.com/abstract=1581364 .

ized cybercrime investigations needs to exclude non-criminal law actions[1] and can only highlight some of the most important issues at stake, with a focused view on specific applications of the principle of proportionality and matters of competence.

II. "Europeanized" Specific Crimes

EU law cannot define crimes on its own. Instead, it can only require member states to penalize certain conduct in its national criminal laws regarding certain types of crimes – terrorism, drug trafficking and organized crime (Art. 31 para. 1 lit. (e) TEU [Treaty on European Union]). These terms are interpreted broadly, and so the EU considers many types of cybercrime to be "organized crime".

A. Framework Decision on attacks against information systems

1. de lege lata

A prime example for European law focusing on matters of substantive criminal law is the aforementioned *FD on attacks against information systems*, which requires member states to penalize certain conduct of illegal access to information systems (Art. 2), illegal system interference (Art. 3), illegal data interference (Art. 4) as well as associated inchoate crimes (Art. 5) (more detailed Bier, 2005: 475; Gercke, 2005). These provisions are – more or less – a limited re-phrasing of the *CoE Cybercrime Convention*, which reaches further and also addresses matters such as the illegal interception of data, misuse of devices, computer-related forgery or fraud, but which also allows for more reservations (Bier, 2005: 474). The exclusion of most procedural aspects in the Framework Decision – besides jurisdiction (Art. 10) – can easily be explained: such issues are typically addressed in the EU by different, generic legal instruments, but need to be included in a CoE convention. But why was an EU instrument needed, if it is a repetition of requirements already spelled out in the CoE convention?

A first difference between these two is in the requirements needed for a state to be fully bound by a legal instrument. A CoE convention is governed by standard public international law, needing formal ratification by states which usually includes a vote in *parliament*. Because of the previous, partial transfer of sovereignty to the EU, a vote in the Council – and thus by representatives of EU member states' *governments* – decides on framework decisions. Secondly, the CoE Cybercrime

[1] For other actions, cf. COM(2007) 267 final; COM(2009) 149 final; OJ C 62, 17.03.2009, p. 16.

Convention had only been ratified by four EU member states[2] at the time of the Framework Decision's enactment. Even up until June 2009 only 15 member states have ratified the CoE Cybercrime Convention (Council of Europe Treaty Office, 2009). With the EU only having very weak political opportunities to pressure member states to ratify – and implement – CoE conventions (Bier, 2005: 474; Gercke, 2006: 285; Sanchez-Hermosilla, 2003: 478), this underlines the need for a binding legal instrument to harmonize a minimum standard of criminal law protection against cybercrime. Thirdly, by enacting own legislation on cybercrime, the EU allows for a more coherent interpretation of other EU instruments such as the *Council Framework Decision 2002/584/JHA of 13 June 2002 on the European arrest warrant and the surrender procedures between Member States* (OJ L 190, 18.07.2002, p. 1, "*EAW FD*") which refer to cybercrime without defining this term themselves (Gröseling and Höfinger, 2007: 550).

With the EU having no strict enforcement mechanism regarding the transformation of framework decisions into national law (Gröseling and Höfinger, 2007: 550), it is not surprising that the EU Commission has found improper implementations in several member states, with seven states not even notifying the Commission at all about their implementation (COM[2008] 448 final; SEC[2009] 765, p. 37). The Commission considers the German implementation (detailed analyses by Gröseling and Höfinger, 2007; Popp, 2007) to be mostly adequate, with the notable exception of § 303b StGB (German Penal Code) – computer sabotage – and specifically its limitation to information systems "of considerable importance for a third party", which is contrary to the framework decision (COM[2008] 448 final, pp. 5-6).

Furthermore, the Commission acknowledges that the real focus on cybercrime needs to be put on newer forms of attacks – such as botnets – and on enhancing and easing of cybercrime investigations. Insofar, while the *FD on attacks against information systems* was an important step forward to extinct *safe harbours* for cyber criminals, its narrow focus on conduct which clearly is worthy of criminalization already on a national level explains its limited importance in practice.[3]

---

[2] The CoE convention had been *signed* by all EU member states except the Czech Republic at that time. Such signatures bind states to a far lesser extent.

[3] Absent in the evaluation is any discussion on the Framework Decision's *legal basis*, Art. 29, 30 para. 1 lit. (a), 31 para. 1 lit. (e) and 34 para. 2 lit. (b) TEU, which was taken into doubt (COM[2005] 583 final) after the notable European Court of Justice (ECJ) decisions on Framework Decisions regarding the protection of the environment (C-176/03 of 13 September 2005 and C-440/05 of 23 October 2007). However, in contrast to those Framework Decisions, this FD does not address areas of EC policy, but instead relates to core criminal law provisions. Therefore, Art. 29 et seq. TEU provide for a proper legal basis for this Framework Decision.

2. de lege ferenda

Therefore, the Commission intends to submit a proposal to modify the *FD on attacks against information systems* in 2009 (COM[2008] 712 final). So far, there is no clear picture of what it will contain besides the criminalization of botnets and distributed denial of service attacks (DDoS)[4], although public statements refer to higher penalties compared to the existing framework decision (FT, 2009). As the usefulness of higher penalties for discouraging criminal behaviour is in doubt (Robinson and Darley, 2003), but a larger correlation to criminal prosecution *at all* exists, its focus should instead be on criminalizing conduct not sufficiently covered yet, and – generally speaking – on the enhancement of cybercrime investigations.

B. Other legislation

Most often, the real issue at stake is not the information system as the object of the crime, but rather the information system being used in the furtherance of another crime such as fraud or illicit content. Such issues are addressed, partly with a special view to the commission of the crime using the Internet, in different, topical legislation, such as the *Council Framework Decision 2004/68/JHA of 22 December 2003 on combating the sexual exploitation of children and child pornography* (OJ L 13, 20.01.2004, p. 44) or the *Council Framework Decision 2008/913/JHA of 28 November 2008 on combating certain forms and expressions of racism and xenophobia by means of criminal law* (OJ L 328 of 06.12.2008, pp. 55-58).

III. Mutual Legal Assistance

The true strength of EU legislation however, is in its enhancement of cooperation between judicial authorities, making prosecutions easier, for example in cases which require access to evidence located in different states – more the rule than the exception in cybercrime cases –, i.e., matters of *mutual legal assistance*. Two different types of EU law regarding mutual legal assistance can be distinguished: most focus, like the *EAW FD*, on the *punishment and enforcement* phase, e.g. by easing the access to suspects, convicts or to proceeds of crime. These instruments, with their generic nature not specific to cybercrime, shall be excluded here. Instead, the few instruments addressing the *obtaining of evidence* shall be analysed.

---

[4] In such cases, each action by itself might be considered too minor to constitute a crime under the existing FD's Art. 3, Art. 4.

A. Starting Point: CoE convention on mutual legal assistance

Unless more specific rules exist, mutual legal assistance between states is based on the following classical concept: sovereign states grant mutual legal assistance case-by-case after a judicial and also an administrative-political decision. While both may be directed or bound by treaties and conventions such as the CoE *European Convention on Mutual Assistance in Criminal Matters of 20 April 1959* (CETS No. 030, "*CoE MLA Convention*"), it remains an issue where courts and governments of both countries are involved. Usually, legal assistance – especially extradition – is denied if the behaviour at stake is not a crime in both states. While referring to this double criminality requirement may be more "friendly" to another state, it shadows and fails to conclusively address the true issues of protecting an *ordre public* of fundamental rights (Vogel, J. and Burchard, C. in Grützner, Pötz and Kreß, 2009: § 2 IRG at 7-22).

B. 2000 MLA Convention and telecommunication surveillance

The *Convention established by the Council in accordance with Article 34 of the Treaty on European Union, on Mutual Assistance in Criminal Matters between the Member States of the European Union* (OJ C 197, 12.07.2000, p. 3, "*2000 MLA Convention*"; cf. the commentary by Grotz in Grützner, Pötz and Kreß, 2009), which is ratified by all EU member states and entered into force with regard to Germany on 02 February 2006, already points ahead towards a new era of mutual legal assistance, with less political interference but more human-rights based safeguards. First, letters rogatory or similar requests for legal assistance may be communicated between competent judicial authorities directly (Art. 6) – thereby, the long and tedious path through official government channels is avoided. Second, it allows for the exchange of information *sua sponte*, i.e. without previous – formal – requests (Art. 7). This permits joint or at least coordinated investigations in several member states. Third, it contains special provisions on telecommunication surveillance (Art. 17-22; cf. Schuster, 2006, regarding telephone surveillance).

Telecommunication, while not defined by the convention, not only includes telephone and telefax, but also all other sorts of electronic and non-electronic (e.g. optical) transmissions of information. Explicitly mentioned during the negotiations were satellite-based telephone communication and the Internet. However, same as in national law, the limits of telecommunication interception need to be taken into account: data which is not part of an ongoing telecommunication, but is stored more or less permanently at one location (PC, Internet Service Provider, remote storage provider or on a "computing cloud") cannot be accessed under these provisions. This is underlined by accessing such data requires more than surveillance, which means passive observance and copying or recording of what is observed.

The convention specifies four distinct – and exclusive[5] – ways regarding the interception and surveillance of telecommunication in trans-border cases:

(1) *Real-Time Interception.* Data is intercepted in one state and immediately transmitted to the authorities of another state (Art. 18 para. 1 lit. (a)) – e.g. all in- and outgoing connections to one Internet server are automatically forwarded in real time.

(2) *Interception and Recording.* Data is intercepted in one state and stored before being transmitted to the authorities of another state. An example may be the storing of all in- and outgoing data packets to one Internet server on a DVD (Art. 18 para. 1 lit. (b)).

(3) *Gateway Interception.* While Art. 19 was originally meant for ground stations of satellite telephone providers, it is also applicable to Virtual Private Network providers and some *Skype* calls, if encrypted Voice-over-IP calls are routed from one state through a gateway in another state to landlines.

(4) *Intelligence.* Finally, Art. 20 addresses the case where one state has technical means to intercept telecommunication within another state – a phenomenon not uncommon in the Internet: for example, traffic may be routed, by accident, chance or on purpose, across multiple states, even if the sender and the recipient are sitting next to each other in the same office.

The limitations regarding telecommunication surveillance depend on the surveillance method and whether the suspect ("subject") is currently present in the state requesting mutual legal assistance. If he is, the investigation is only limited by the requesting state's procedure law, especially if real-time interception is possible. The convention itself only spells out certain formalities (Art. 18 para. 3, 6).

Whenever the suspect is in the state which is to execute the surveillance, it may deny the execution of telecommunication surveillance by methods (1) and (2) in cases where the executing state's law does not allow for telecommunication surveillance in a comparable situation (Art. 18 para. 4, para. 5 (b)). As long as this optional ground for refusal is utilized – which typically is the case –, telecommunication surveillance must be permissible both under the law of the requesting state and of the executing state. In the German transposition, this is seen not only as a factual criterion – meaning all the requirements of § 100a StPO (German law on criminal

[5] Following from its focus on surveillance of telecommunication, these provisions do not cover remote searches: be it the access to a remote, Internet storage located in another state in the wake of an overt house search, be it the hacking into a computer located in another state to access the raw, unencrypted communication data before it is encrypted and sent to a recipient (so-called "telecommunication surveillance at the source"), or be it the access to an e-mail inbox at an ISP located abroad (LG Hamburg, Decision of 2008-01-08 – 619 Qs 1/08; Gaede, 2008). For such cases, states need to fall back to default rules of mutual legal assistance, as e.g. provided by the CoE MLA Convention.

procedure) are to be met, including a heightened level of suspicion for a list offence. Instead, it is also seen as a procedural criterion, so that typically another – German – judicial order is required under § 100b para. 1 StPO, §§ 59 para. 3, 77 para. 1 IRG (German law on mutual legal assistance in criminal matters) (Schuster, 2006: 659; see also Wilkitzki, P. in Grützner, Pötz and Kreß, 2009: § 59 IRG at 20, footnote 7; RiVASt [German Guidelines on Relations with Foreign Countries in Criminal Law Matters] Nr. 77a).

If intelligence-based surveillance methods are used, or the surveillance targets a subject who is present in a third country, the affected country is to be notified about the surveillance. Only in the case of intelligence-based surveillance may it order the stopping of the surveillance (Art. 20 para. 4) if its own law does not allow for it in a comparable situation or if the surveillance contradicts its national *ordre public.*

In Art. 23, the convention also addresses the question of the follow-up protection of the data obtained by telecommunication surveillance – e.g. its use for the prosecution of another crime uncovered by chance by the surveillance, or for police work. As long as the data originated in the same state, it is free to use it according to national law even if it was obtained with the help of another state (Art. 23 para. 6). Otherwise – e.g. e-mails between two subjects residing in another state have been monitored – the data obtained may be used for *any other* proceedings covered by the convention, meaning all criminal proceedings referred to in Art. 1 as well as the other proceedings mentioned in Art. 3. In stark contrast to the limits to other uses (Art. 23 para. 1 lit. (b) and (c)) this does not provide for a procedural safeguard on its own. However, such requirements may optionally be introduced at the time of the transmittal of data (Art. 18 para. 5 lit. (b), Art. 23 para. 4).

C. Borderless telecommunication surveillance?

Does this mean that telecommunication surveillance through intelligence methods is allowed not only without any state borders, but also without any safeguards or limitations? While the convention does not spell out specifics, other European law does and requires national law to provide for a sufficient minimum standard for all cases of telecommunication surveillance because of the common principle (Art. 6 para. 1 TEU) of proportionality (Calliess, in: Calliess and Ruffert, 2007: Art. 6 TEU at 75). In combination with special fundamental rights such as the right to privacy specified in Art. 8 ECHR (Convention for the Protection of Human Rights and Fundamental Freedoms, CETS No. 5)[6], a common European understanding is forming insofar as telecommunication surveillance may only be ordered for a *lim-*

[6] While the EU is not – yet – a member state of the ECHR, all EU member states are. Therefore, the ECHR is also seen as a reflection of the common principles referenced in Art. 6 para. 1 TEU.

ited duration, only in cases where a *severe crime* is presumed, only if a *deletion procedure* exists if the suspicion does not materialize, and only if *sufficient independent oversight* is guaranteed (cf. Grabenwarter, 2008: § 22 at 34 and the jurisprudence of the ECtHR [European Court of Human Rights], e.g. in its judgement of 2003-02-18, *Prado Bugallo,* Nr. 58496/00). For all this, it is irrelevant whether the monitoring is intra- or extra-territorial (cf. Grabenwarter, 2008: § 17 at 12-13).

At least regarding their core, these principles can be seen as part of the European *ordre public* which serves as an implied or sometimes explicit limitation to treaty-, convention- or framework decision-based mutual legal assistance, not only with regard to telecommunication surveillance. Moreover, this European *ordre public* and its principle of proportionality also include protection against an overly broad and disproportional follow-up use of data.

D. MLA Framework Decisions and the Obtaining of Evidence

The two Framework Decisions which focus on the obtaining and transfer of evidence – the *Council Framework Decision 2003/577/JHA of 22 July 2003 on the execution in the European Union of orders freezing property or evidence* (OJ L 196 of 02.11.2003, p. 45, "*EFO FD*") and the *Council Framework Decision 2008/978/JHA of 18 December 2008 on the European evidence warrant for the purpose of obtaining objects, documents and data for use in proceedings in criminal matters* (OJ L 350 of 30.12.2008, p. 72., "*EEW FD*") – have been decided upon and implemented in member states so slowly that critics such as the Commission consider those to be "somewhat 'virtual'" and therefore of few use (COM [2009] 262 final, p. 3). Nonetheless, their normatively surprisingly sharp teeth need to be taken into account when analysing future proposals.

While the *EFO FD* (cf. also the commentary by Böse, M. in Grützner, Pötz and Kreß, 2009) prohibits any double criminality test regarding cybercrime-related searches and confiscations with a view to a later use the evidence in another country, it does not make away with an additional test in the executing state which may reject disproportionate orders (cf. Art. 6 TEU and Art. 1 of the *EFO FD*) or prescribe other, formal requirements, such as the German provision that postal mail only may be opened by judges or public prosecutors, not by police (Art. 5 para. 2, §§ 99, 100 StPO). The scope of this Framework Decision applies to any "data which could be produced as evidence in criminal proceedings" (Art. 2 lit. (e)) which is overly broad: regarding the *location*, the data may be stored on a computer of the subject – even located within his house –, it may be stored as an e-mail at an internet service provider the subject uses, it may even be a database of credit card transactions stored at the data processing facility of a financial institution. Regarding the *content*, communication data or metadata is not excluded, same as confidential data ranging from financial transactions over medical data to core areas of private life. Limitations stem, however, both from national laws and its immunities (Art. 7 para. 1 lit. (b)) which the Framework Decision recognizes unconditionally, from its restriction to open freezing instead of secret hacking to access data, and from the aforementioned European *ordre public* as an implicit limitation.

Another limitation used to exist in the actual transfer of evidence, the second step after the obtaining of evidence, still being governed by classical mutual legal assistance regime. However, Art. 10 para. 3, national law such as § 97 IRG and the new *EEW FD* (Kotzurek, 2006; Krüßmann, 2008) move this phase towards the principle of mutual trust and mutual recognition. With the broad opportunities to first use a *European Freezing Order*, the limitation of its scope in Art. 4 para. 2 to exclude the *obtaining* of certain types of data can easily be circumvented. A double criminality requirement is not applicable at all for pre-existing data and for cyber-crime-related search or seizure *Evidence Warrants* (Art. 14 para. 2). In its safe-guards, however, the *EEW FD* spells out, for the first time, specific and firm rules following from the proportionality principle in its Art. 7. While those are less ambitious than the original *EEW FD* proposed, they explicitly acknowledge a need for a more specific European standard on procedural rights in criminal investigations.

E. The Future: European Evidence Warrant II

With the slow implementation of the *EFO FD,* the only recent decision on the *EEW FD*, and a complaint by practitioners that the *CoE European Convention on Mutual Assistance in Criminal Matters* is more useful in practice because of its less complex nature, the Commission has set itself an ambitious goal of replacing the current, incoherent set of rules on trans-national obtaining of evidence with a new *European Evidence Warrant II Framework Decision* (COM[2009] 262 final, p. 17, "*EEW II FD*"). While such fast action – before the *EEW FD* implementation period has even ended – does not square with the aim of evaluation-based EU policy (COM[2009] 262 final, p. 10), it addresses the known inconsistency of the *acquis.*

Much about the new *EEW II FD* is still unknown. As a first step a *Green Paper* is to be tabled by the Commission in summer 2009. Nonetheless, a few general ideas and concepts have already been floated, most notably in the Commission's input for the Stockholm Programme[7] (COM[2009] 262 final, p. 17). First, the *EEW II FD* will focus at the *obtaining* of data, including data explicitly excluded by the *EEW FD*. Second, it will put special emphasis on *electronic evidence*. Third, there will be very *few grounds for refusing* to execute an *EEW II*, but as was already

---

[7] The Stockholm Programme will, as the successor of the Tampere and Hague Programme, specify the policy aims and action plan for the EU in the area of freedom, security and justice. It is to be adopted by the European Council in December 2009.

mentioned above, the classic reason for refusal – lack of double criminality – is often not on the point to provide for specific protection of human rights.

Fourthly, the Commission has become increasingly aware of the need for the issuing state to honour the principle of proportionality, as can be seen in the *Final report on the fourth round of mutual evaluations – The practical application of the EAW* (Council Document 8302/4/09, p. 15). Additionally, asserting the proportionality of intrusions into privacy will become even more important for it is a requirement set forth by the ECHR which the EU is bound to adhere to[8]. With a view to *evidence,* it must therefore be up to the judicial authority issuing an order to obtain evidence to apply the proportionality principle. Tackling the issue of proportionality at the issuing stage is also coherent with the principle of availability, which disfavours any blocking of data obtained previously and lawfully.

F. A Requirement of Proportionality in EEW II

However, merely specifying that the obtaining of evidence must be proportionate and referring the specifics to jurisprudence is not a proper way to proceed: first, such jurisprudence and judicial oversight by the ECJ is necessarily always one step behind. Second, there are often only low barriers to introduce evidence obtained in violation of the proportionality principle. Therefore, it would be quite uncommon for the ECJ – or the ECtHR – to get a chance to rule on the proportionality requirements regarding the obtaining of specific types of evidence. Third, large discrepancies between the application of the proportionality principle in different member states may be the consequence, which may then reduce the mutual trust which is needed as basis for mutual recognition and thus for the long-term success of the *EEW II FD*. Fourth, it is also more efficient to specify to judicial authorities certain basic limitations which *at least* have to be fulfilled for a surveillance measure to be proportionate – and thus not requiring them tedious studies of the matters at stake for each and every case. Studies for which they may not have sufficient time especially in the heat of ongoing investigations where quick actions are required! Therefore, defining more specific rules on what is proportionate should be included in the *EEW II FD.* Such rules may combine procedural aspects (such as judicial and parliamentary oversight, time limits and deletion procedures) with material aspects (such as a heightened level of suspicion or the limitation to certain types of crimes). What is more, any specific limitations provided for by the *EEW II FD* should also be adhered to in purely national cases in order to allow for a later

---

[8] Ratifying the ECHR is actually the first and foremost issue mentioned in the Commission's input to the Stockholm Programme, albeit it requires the ratification and entry into force of the *Lisbon Treaty*. Until then, the EU is only indirectly bound by the ECHR (cf. footnote 6).

transfer of the evidence to another state, without violating the European principle of proportionality, and without violating the principle of availability.

For such rules to be specific enough and therefore to be efficient, they need to take into account the implications of different types of evidence. Looking at electronic evidence *strictu sensu* (and not at other types of evidence such as DNA or fingerprints merely stored digitally), one can distinguish at least five types of computer-related evidence alone, each with different intrusions into fundamental rights and therefore different requirements under the proportionality principle.

(1) *Telecommunication surveillance.* The jurisprudence of the ECtHR already having defined several limitations can and should serve as a starting point for proper safeguards, which therefore are to require a limitation to cases where severe crimes are presumed, deletion procedures exist, and a judicial order or at least judicial oversight as well as protection of communication with (lawyerly, medical or religious) counselling and communication concerning the most intimate matters of life are guaranteed.

(2) *Telecommunication data retention.* This is perhaps *the* issue most suitable for a European law on obtaining evidence – after all, the storing of data is already an obligation created by European law. Data stored from the whole and mostly innocent population has a deterrent effect not only on crime, but also on legitimate and even highly useful conduct such as anonymous counselling. These issues alone warrant a limitation to the use of retained data. Also, the different types of retained information should also be taken into account: the *IP* address probably being the least, and e-mail and telephone communication partners being the most sensitive.

(3) *Open search and seizure.* Access to electronic data stored on hard disks during a lawful, open search, which was ordered by a judicial authority, has comparably limited implications, even if the storage device happens to be located remotely, even in a foreign country. In such cases, the implications for the other state are similar to the "intelligence" access to ongoing telecommunication data, as provided for by Art. 20, *2000 MLA Convention.* Therefore, requiring the agreement of the other state involved, such as proposed by the Council (Council Document 15569/08, p. 5), is inconsistent. The *use* of the data obtained must obey the proportionality principle and other safeguards. This may mean that data stored for others (e.g. if the search or seizure is at an Internet Service Provider, and the data obtained contains email communication between third parties) is off-limits, same as archived communication with medical doctors or defence counsel.

(4) *Hidden search and seizure.* Be it by state-initiated hacking or by accessing data at an intermediate or storage provider, any obtaining of data unknown to the suspect creates the danger that his side is never heard in a court of

law. Additional dangers of illicit, disproportionate and excessive access to data, and dangers of tampering with evidence (and thus lowering the quality of electronic evidence in general) are caused by state-initiated hacking into a suspect's computer system. Therefore, much higher limitations with much stronger oversight are needed compared to open search and seizure operations (cf. the aforementioned Decision of the German Constitutional Court of 27 February 2008 – 1 BvR 370/07, 1 BvR 595/07 – "Online-Durchsuchung" and the associated, ongoing debate in jurisprudence).

(5) *Data mining.* Be it the combination of multiple sources, be it the search of one extremely extensive source (such as the information stored at Google) – one can learn nearly anything about many people by combining the different bits and pieces of electronic trails. This is wholly different to the state knowing all details about a specific crime, which is a necessity for criminal investigations. The more data is combined (independent of its source), the more any off-the-norm, legitimate behaviour becomes suspicious in and by itself. Also, most worrisome is such a wealth of information in the wrong hands – and it is also the duty of a state obeying the rule of law to protect against itself becoming an instrument for wrong hands, or of becoming a wrong hand itself. Therefore, restraint in combining different data outside of specific cases is of essential importance. Only if such *data mining* is limited to the most severe issues (international terrorism with weapons of mass destruction and comparable crimes), subject to scrutiny and powerful oversight, and immediate deletion of data obtained but no longer used is guaranteed, negative implications and severe risks to society can be mitigated.

Addressing all these issues – also for non-electronic evidence – in one single instrument is an ambitious task, so dealing with generic issues first and then adding specific, short instruments may turn out to be more practical.

III. Cybercrime Investigations

Among laymen, hackers and crackers, the EU is most known in the field of cybercrime investigations for its *Directive 2006/24/EC on the retention of data generated or processed in connection with the provision of publicly available electronic communications services or of public communications networks* (OJ L 105, 13.04.2006, p. 54, "*Data Retention Directive*"), which is based on the common market for telecommunication providers – and thus not on criminal procedure competences – and which proscribes, *inter alia,* the storing of IP addresses and their users for at least six months: a most useful tool for cybercrime investigations.

A. Investigation Techniques

But even besides the *Data Retention Directive*, two off-topic framework decision proposals need to be at the centre of discussing future EU actions on cybercrime investigations, as they contain unprecedented references to investigation techniques such as telephone surveillance. Whether highly condemnable crimes are used as a "test vehicle" to further EU legislation in this field, or whether it merely stems from practical needs to investigate these heinous crimes, is a matter of political interpretation and analysis. Here the legal issues at stake shall be analysed instead.

1. Updated Framework Decision on Combating Trafficking in Human Beings

According to a March 2009 Commission *Proposal for a Council Framework Decision on preventing and combating trafficking in human beings, and protecting victims, repealing Framework Decision 2002/629/JHA* (COM[2009] 136 final), member states shall „take the necessary measures to ensure that investigative tools which are used in organized crime cases such as phone tapping, electronic surveillance, and financial investigation are available" (Art. 7 para. 4). As the *Council Framework Decision 2008/841/JHA of 24 October 2008 on the fight against organised crime* (OJ L 300 of 11.11.2008, p. 42) does not contain anything at all regarding investigation techniques, but it is widely known that states allow the furthest-reaching investigation techniques for terrorism and organized crime, it creates an *indirect* requirement to enhance the investigation techniques in cases of trafficking in human beings. Because of its systematic link to phone tapping and its contemporary link to existing surveillance laws in national law, "phone tapping and electronic surveillance" needs to be considered as an equivalent to what the *2000 MLA Convention* calls telecommunication surveillance.

2. Updated Framework Decision on Combating Child Pornography

Another Commission *Proposal for a Council Framework Decision on combating the sexual abuse, sexual exploitation of children and child pornography, repealing Framework Decision 2004/68/JHA* (COM[2009] 135 final) of the same date goes even beyond that, as member states are to take the "necessary measures to ensure effective investigation and prosecution ..., allowing thc possibility of covert operations at least in those cases where the use of an information system is involved" (Art. 12 para. 5). Surely "covert operations" includes "covert investigations" – "investigations into crimes by officers acting under covert or false identities" (Art. 14 para. 1, *2000 MLA Convention*) – but the lack of any further definition or guidance leaves open whether it also requires covert, technical means such as the installation of keyloggers, trojan horses or the hacking into computer systems (cf. the discussion in German police law regarding "Online-Durchsuchung" mentioned above). Furthermore, such a specific, *direct* requirement regarding an investigation technique should also be accompanied with specific procedural safeguards and limitations based on fundamental rights and the principle of proportionality, as a mere implicit, generic link to Art. 6 TEU and thus to the ECHR fails to reflect the importance of these safeguards and only leave room for an ex-post evaluation of the safeguards on the European level by jurisprudence of the ECtHR and the ECJ.

3. EU Competence for Investigation Technique Obligations?

The legal basis for such direct or indirect requirements to provide for investigation techniques is doubtful: The proposal explanations mention Art. 31 para. 1 lit. (e), which only refers to "constituent elements of criminal acts and to penalties" and thus to matters of criminal law and not criminal procedure. Art. 34 para. 2 lit. (b) refers to the type of legislation, but the third provision specified, Art. 29 also mentions "closer cooperation" between police forces, judicial and other competent authorities. The *sedes materiae* of the proposed rules is national law on investigation techniques and not any waiving of double criminality in cross-border investigations. Even though cross-border investigations might become legal in some rare cases,[9] these rules are not on the spot for "closer cooperation" and associated "compatibility", which means Art. 31 para. 1 lit. (a), lit. (c) are not valid legal bases. Not even the open wording of Art. 31 para. 1 – that common actions "include" what is specified in lit. (a) to (e) – suffices, for these provisions focus beyond any cooperation aspect. Therefore, however useful and necessary these provisions may be, they cannot be considered permissible under current EU primary law.

In contrast, the upcoming *Lisbon Treaty* and its Art. 82 *Treaty on the Functioning of the European Union* (TFU) allows for harmonization of criminal procedure – first and foremost with regard to limitations to investigations from a suspect's point of view (para. 2 lit. (b)), but also generically (lit. (d)). Based on this viewpoint, it is self-evident that rules on investigation techniques must include some safeguards.

4. European Information Systems Architecture

A most worrisome development is the intended creation of an European information systems architecture (COM[2009] 262 final, p. 16) based on the principle of availability, meaning unhindered access by European institutions and member states to data stored by the states for any legitimate, police or judicial purpose. As shown above, such data mining, which the Commission intends to research and

---

9 The *2000 MLA Convention* still requires phone tapping to be permissible under both states' law, which would be guaranteed by the *FD* proposals.

promote, has such high implications in terms of fundamental rights that pronounced restraint is required in utilizing such tools, and even in preparatory steps.

B. Coordination

Besides all requirements of national laws, the European Union also coordinates investigations at the European level, especially using *Europol, Eurojust* but also an *European Judicial Network (EJN).*

1. National Contact Points

Focused on Cybercrime, this is supplemented by the *Council Recommendation of 25 June 2001 on contact points maintaining a 24-hour service for combating high-tech crime* (OJ C 187, 03.07.2001, p. 5) which tries to address the need for quick, transnational reactions in certain cybercrime investigations, such as quick freezes of volatile data. Its implementation and usefulness in practice need to be seen as shadowy: while the Recommendation itself speaks about an extension of the pre-existing G8 network for combating high-tech crime – which also serves as the basis for the CoE Cybercrime Convention and its 24/7-network (Art. 35) – both the evaluation of the *FD on attacks against information systems* and the 2007 Council Conclusions "Combating Cybercrime" (Council Document 14617/07, p. 20) hint at different and partly inefficient contact points being used, creating unnecessary frictions and delays in cybercrime investigations.

2. "Pooling" and Europeanizing Investigations

One might be tempted to consider the "pooling" of investigations by using Joint Investigation Teams (JIT), or informal "shadow", "mirror" proceedings in different member states of the same crime – and extensive information sharing between the states involved – as merely an organizational matter. However, if safeguards are not upheld during the *obtaining* phase, they could be avoided by "forum shopping" for the most permissible *obtaining* regime, and later utilizing the most permissible regime for *introducing* evidence in court.

In the medium term, such "pooling" of investigations and of the authority to conduct investigations might also be taken one step further, vesting the current "coordinators" Europol and Eurojust with the right to exercise the "pooled" authorities in any of the involved states such as they choose.

In the long term, the *Lisbon Treaty* offers for yet a further step: if at least nine member states wish to do so, Art. 86 para. 1 *Treaty on the Functioning of the European Union* (TFU) allows them to empower Eurojust to become the European Public

Prosecutor's Office (EPP). While its competence is at first limited to the protection of the EU's financial interests, it can be extended to include other "serious crimes having a cross-border dimension" (Art. 86 para. 4 TFU). International, high-profile cybercrime with its intrinsic borderless character could very well be one of the most important issues where an EPP is needed, albeit under a principle of complementarity with national prosecution. The EPP will have its own Rules of Procedure (Art. 86 para. 3). How its rules on obtaining and introduction of evidence are to be squared with the provision that actions are to be brought forward in national criminal courts (Art. 86 para. 2) still needs to be seen. Such a genuinely European institution and such genuinely European investigations would, of course, be fully bound by European fundamental rights principles and especially the proportionality principle.

IV. Conclusion

A wide breadth of cybercrime-related issues is tackled by European Union criminal law and criminal procedure – from penalizing obligations regarding illicit conduct, instruments addressing the investigation phase which often needs mutual legal assistance in cybercrime cases, to the promotion of the *enforcement* of punishments by means of the *EAW FD*. But do they sum up to a coherent approach?

Different levels and methods of safeguards regarding the investigation phase alone – from implicit limitations to national law stemming from Art. 6 TEU via the indirect protection provided by double criminality to explicit references in Art. 7 of the *EAW FD* –, the lack of a discussion on what is *permissible* in the Internet – for example with regard to freedom of speech, fair use of copyright-protected material – and on matters of *jurisdiction*[10] show that many steps are to be taken to reach the ambitious goal of a "concerted" strategy to combat cybercrime while protecting fundamental rights and freedoms. Furthermore, underestimated instruments such as the *EFO FD* require sufficient implementation in national law (which it lacks in at least nine member states), else all their theoretical, "virtual" strength is moot.

Whether this indeed leads to a safer European Union is not only a matter of whether more criminals can be identified and convicted. It is also a matter whether the people can feel safe from disproportionate interference by their own states and by other European states. Specifying such requirements based on the principle of proportionality for different types of evidence may enhance the mutual trust of states, but also the trust of individuals in not only their own state, but in the whole group of states forming an ever closer Union.

---

[10] As the proposal for a *Council Framework Decision on prevention and settlement of conflicts of exercise of jurisdiction in criminal matters* (Council Document 8535/09) limits itself to cases where two or more states intend to prosecute, it does not provide a sufficient solution.

REFERENCES

All EU COM, Council and OJ documents referenced within this article are available online from the World Wide Web: <http://eurocrim.jura.uni-tuebingen.de/>.

- BIER, S. 2005. Kampf gegen Cyberkriminalität. *Datenschutz und Datensicherheit*. 29, pp. 473-477.
- CALLIES, C. and M. RUFFERT. 2007. *EUV, EGV. Das Verfassungsrecht der Europäischen Union mit Europäischer Grundrechtecharta. Kommentar. 3rd edition.* München: Beck.
- COUNCIL OF EUROPE TREATY OFFICE. 2009. Convention on Cybercrime. Chart of signatures and ratifications [online]. [Accessed 9 July 2009]. Available from World Wide Web: <http://conventions.coe.int/Treaty/Commun/ChercheSig.asp?NT=185&CL=ENG>.
- FT. 2009. EU plans tougher cybercrime laws [online]. [Accessed 9 July 2009]. Available from World Wide Web: <http://www.ft.com/cms/s/0/10a407b6-5913-11de-80b3-00144feabdc0.html>
- GAEDE, K. 2008. Der grundrechtliche Schutz gespeicherter E-Mails beim Provider und ihre weltweite strafprozessuale Überwachung. *Strafverteidiger*. 2009(2), pp. 96-102
- GERCKE, M. 2005. Der Rahmenbeschluss über Angriffe auf Informationssysteme. *Computer und Recht*. 2005(6), pp. 468-472.
- GERCKE, M. 2006. Die Entwicklung des Internetstrafrechts im Jahr 2005. *Zeitschrift für Urheber- und Medienrecht*. 2006(4), pp. 284-294.
- GRABENWARTER, C. 2008. *Europäische Menschenrechtskonvention. 3rd edition.* München: Beck.
- GRÖSELING, N. and F.M. HÖFINGER. 2007. Hacking und Computerspionage - Auswirkungen des 41. StrÄndG zur Bekämpfung der Computerkriminalitä. *Multimedia und Recht*. 2007(9), pp. 549-553.
- GRÜTZNER, H., P.-G. PÖTZ and C. KRESS. 2009. *Internationaler Rechtshilfeverkehr in Strafsachen.* 3rd edition. Heidelberg: C.F. Müller.
- KOTZUREK, N. 2006. Gegenseitige Anerkennung und Schutzgarantien bei der Europäischen Beweisanordnung. *Zeitschrift für Internationale Strafrechtsdogmatik.* 2006(3), pp. 123-139.
- KRUESSMANN, T. 2008. Grenzüberschreitender Beweistransfer durch Europäische Beweisanordnung? *Strafverteidiger Forum*. 2008(11), pp. 458-463.
- POPP, A. 2007. Computerstrafrecht in Europa. *Medien und Recht International.* 2007, pp. 84-88.
- ROBINSON, P. H. and J. M. HARLEY. 2003. The Role of Deterrence in the Formulation of Criminal Law Rules: At Its Worst When Doing Its Best, *Georgetown Law Journal.* 91, pp. 949-1002.
- SANCHEZ-HERMOSILLA, F. 2003. Neues Strafrecht für den Kampf gegen Computerkriminalität. *Computer und Recht*. 2003(10), pp. 774-780.
- SCHUSTER, F. P. 2006. Telekommunikationsüberwachung in grenzüberschreitenden Strafverfahren nach Inkrafttreten des EU-Rechtshilfeübereinkommens. Neue Zeitschrift für Strafrecht. 2006(12), pp. 657-663.

Conference Program

Tuesday, 12 May 2009

14:00 Welcome Address

PROF. DR. DRES. H.C. ULRICH SIEBER
Max Planck Institute for Foreign and International Criminal Law,
Director at the Institute

14:10 Introduction to the Conference: Contemporary Questions in IT Security

DR. PHILLIP W. BRUNST
Max Planck Institute for Foreign and International Criminal Law,
Head of Section 'Information Law and Legal Informatics'

14:30 Underground Economy – The Business of Cybercrime

JAN SPOENLE
Max Planck Institute for Foreign and International Criminal Law,
Researcher in Section 'Information Law and Legal Informatics'

15:30 Attacks on Critical Infrastructure

DR. MARCO GERCKE
Lecturer at the University of Cologne/Germany

16:30 Mass SMS Chat Frauds

HANS-PETER MERKEL
Forensic Expert in March/Germany

17:30 Cyber Security and Privacy

LAUREN SAADAT
Associate Director, International Privacy Policy
U.S. Department of Homeland Security

18:30 Conclusions of the First Day

PROF. DR. DAVID WALL
Chair for Criminal Justice and Information Technology
University of Leeds/UK

Wednesday, 13 May 2009

9:00 Alterations in Danger-Awareness along the Info Communication Revolution

DR. KATALIN PARTI
Hungarian National Institute of Criminology

10:00 Notebook Security

MARTIN FILLERS
ITSC-Manager
Dell Halle GmbH/Germany

11:00 Laymen's Responsibility for IT Security

MEINRAD ROMBACH
Computer Academy for Lifelong Learning/Germany

12:00 Lunch Break

14:00 Cybercrime and the Organization of Crime Online

PROF. DR. DAVID WALL
Chair for Criminal Justice and Information Technology
University of Leeds/UK

15:00 Cybercrime against Businesses

RAMONA RANTALA
Statistician at the Bureau of Justice Statistics
U.S. Department of Justice

16:00 Criminal Justice Systems' (Over) Reactions to Cyber Security Threats

DR. ALEŠ ZAVRŠNIK
Institute of Criminology at the Faculty of Law
Ljubljana/Slovenia

17:00 Abuse – the other Side of the Coin

AMIR ALSBIH
Kabel BW/Germany

18:00 Consequences of Cloud Computing

PROF. DR. GERHARD SCHNEIDER
Chair for Communication Systems and
Chief Information Officer
University of Freiburg/Germany

19:00 Conclusions of the Second Day

DR. SOUMYO MOITRA
CERT/Software
Enineering Institute at Carnegie Mellon University/U.S.A.

Thursday, 14 May 2009

9:00 Internet Policy and Security Management

DR. SOUMYO MOITRA
Cert/Software
Enineering Institute at Carnegie Mellon University/U.S.A.

10:00 Next Generation Firewallling

ANDREAS MAYER
Indevis/Germany

11:00 Hack the Max Planck Institute

JOCHEN JÄHNKE
Max Planck Institute for Foreign and International Criminal Law,
Head of IT

12:00 Negligent Security at International Speech and Data Communication

MARKUS WÖHRLE
DataDirect/Germany

13:00 GSM and DECT Security

DR. DIRK VON SUCHODOLETZ
Chair for Communication Systems
University of Freiburg/Germany

14:00 Conclusions of the Third Day

DR. KATALIN PARTI
Hungarian National Institute of Criminology

14:30 Closing of the Conference

MARCELLO BELLINI/DR. PHILLIP BRUNST/JOCHEN JÄHNKE

About the Authors

Dominik Brodowski is a senior research assistant at the Chair of European Criminal Law and Criminal Procedure, Professor Dr Joachim Vogel. In addition, he is a graduate student of law at the Eberhard Karls Universität Tübingen, Germany and a graduate of the University of Pennsylvania Law School. His professional activities focus on European criminal law, criminal procedure and its interaction with constitutional law.

Dr. *Phillip W. Brunst* is a senior researcher at the Max Planck Institute for Foreign and International Criminal Law where he heads the section 'Information Law and Legal Informatics'. He is interested in the phenomena of cybercrime as well as the (mainly international) instruments in the fight against them. He current research focus regards the danger of terrorist activities on the Internet. He teaches at the universities of Freiburg and Munich and served as expert or lecturer at numerous national as well as international institutions. Further information is available on his website at http://www.pbrunst.de

Jochen Jähnke, M.A. is Head of the IT section at the Max Planck Institute for Foreign and International Criminal Law in Freiburg, Germany. He studied chemistry, mathematics, sociology, psychology, and computer science at the universities of Stuttgart and Freiburg and received his masters's degree in computer science, psychology, and sociology. His research interests cover various technical, sociological, and criminological topics of information technology – ranging from the social impact of the Internet to cybercrime and the security of information infrastructures.

Soumyo Darshan Moitra, Ph.D., is a Senior Member of Technical Staff at the Software Engineering Institute, Carnegie Mellon University. Prior to that, he was a professor at the Indian institute of Technology. He has taught at Baruch College, New York and was a Member of Technical Staff at Bell Communications Research. He has been an Alexander von Humboldt Fellow at the Max Planck Institute and an Invited Professor at NTT Laboratories in Tokyo. He obtained his B.Sc. from the University of Sussex, an M.A. from Cornell University, an M.S. from Syracuse University and a Ph.D. from Carnegie Mellon University. He has published papers in the areas of Policy Analysis, Criminal Justice, Operations Research, Telecommunications, Technology Management and Cybercrime.

Kataliln Parti, Ph.D., is a lawyer and a research fellow of National Institute of Criminology, Hungary. She received a PhD in the topic of the obstacles of applying criminal law in regulating online pornography. She is the author of numerous articles and a presenter at international events on criminology such as the European Society of Criminology's annual conferences. She is a lecturer of Károli Gáspár Protestant University Budapest on criminology, criminological aspects of cybercrime and cyber pornography. She has European certificates on CEOP's Expert Training for Internet Child Sex Offenders and Cybex's European Certificate on Cybercrime and Electronic Evidence. Her current research field is the influence of the infocommunication development on human contacts, types of communication and morality, surveillance and virtual reality.

Ramona Rantala has been a Statistician at the Bureau of Justice Statistics since 1997. As manager of the National Computer Security Survey, she has analyzed and reported on the nature, scope, and consequences of cybercrime against the nation's businesses. Ms. Rantala serves on several federal committees, including the Confidentiality and Data Access Committee, the American Community Survey committee, the Data.gov committee, and is the BJS liaison to the American Statistical Association's Committee on Law and Justice Statistics. She also oversees the National Archive of Criminal Justice Data at the University of Michigan and has served as a guest lecturer in numerous criminal justice and sociology classes at the George Washington University as well as at the Quantitative Analysis of Crime and Criminal Justice Statistics Summer Workshop at the University of Michigan.

Meinrad Rombach M.A. is owner of CALL - Computer Academy for Lifelong Learning, a provider for near-workplace online trainings and virtual classroom support. After graduation in physics he researched on human-machine interaction and secrecy-proof data storage in medicine. He has a 25 years background as computer trainer and a long practise as the neighborhood´s private IT emergency troubleshooting taskforce. He is member of Freiburg´s IT security initiative FRITSI and supervising coach for the ISO/IEC 17024 certificate "IT security coordinator".

Prof. Dr. *Gerhard Schneider* is professor for communication systems and director of the University computing centre. Thus his research focuses on the early adoption of new trends into a computer centre production environment. As vice-rector of the university (2003 to 2008) he was in charge of the University's IT and New Media policy. He served on a number of national commitees, such as the IT commitee and the Library board of the Deutsche Forschungsgemeinschaft DFG, and is a member of the "legal issues" research group of the Deutsche Forschungsnetz DFN. He can be contacted at director@rz.uni-freiburg.de.

Jan Spoenle is working as a researcher in the section 'information law and legal informatics' at the Max Planck Institute for Foreign and International Criminal Law. He specializies in Information law and criminal procedure law. His main interest are cybercrime and cyberterrorism, their phenomenology and ways to combat these threats legally and technically. His dissertation project examines the legal and practical problems in prosecuting cybercrime.

Dr. *Dirk von Suchodoletz* works as assistant at the professorship of communication systems of the Institute for Computer Science at Freiburg University. Beside the research in communication and telephony networks he is teaching seminars, student projects and is looking after the students' scientific work and theses. He studied math, economics, and politics at the Georg August University of Goettingen and graduated in mathematics in 2002. He received his doctoral degree in 2008 at the technical faculty. The author can be contacted at dirk.von.suchodoletz@rz.uni-freiburg.de.

Prof. *David S. Wall* (BA, MA, M Phil, PhD, FRSA, AcSS) is Professor of Criminology at the University of Durham, he was formerly Professor of Criminal Justice and Information Society at the University of Leeds where was also Head of the School of Law. He conducts research and teaches in the fields of cybercrime, criminal justice and information technology, policing and intellectual property crime. He has published a wide range of reports, articles and books on these subjects which include: Cybercrime: The Transformation of Crime in the Information Age (Polity, 2007).

Dr. *Aleš Završnik,* Assistant Professor, is a researcher at the Institute of Criminology at the Faculty of Law in Ljubljana. He focuses on issues related to philosophy of criminal law and "crime and technology" nexus and has recently published a book "Homo Criminalis: Images of a Criminal in High-Tech Risk Society". He regularly publishes in the leading Slovenian law criminological journal Revija za kriminalistiko in kriminologijo and contributes papers at various international scientific conferences. He is a MC member of the COST Action "Living in Surveillance Societies" and the COST Action "Cyberbullying". He is regularly cooperating with researchers from the "Vienna Group" on issues related to cyberlaw and researchers from other Balkan countries and he has organized several high-level conferences. His scientific work was supported by the Central European University (2007), World Federation of Scientists (2008) and the Max-Planck-Institute for Foreign and International Criminal Law (2009).